Childhood Development

by Joan Martin
& Edith Witmer

Taking the Neurological
Voyage to Maturity

Cover Design
    Joseph Ebersole, Illustra Graphics, Bedford, Pennsylvania
    www.illustra-graphics.com

Inside Artwork
    Virginia Kreider

Joan lives in Lancaster County, Pennsylvania. She has pioneered neurophysiological therapy among the plain people, and works full time from her home office. She is involved with special ed workshops and is happy to do anything to bless the children she loves. She is extensively involved with her mother, her siblings and their families and is a very beloved "auntie". Joan thrives on spending time with her friends.

Edith lives with her husband Eldon in Snyder County, Pennsylvania, and is the mother of three grown children, with nine grandchildren. She enjoys being a homemaker and a grandmother. Edith also works as a neurophysiological therapist and as a counselor. She enjoys music, flowers, writing and connecting with others.

Contact Information:

Joan Martin
121 E. 28th Division Hwy.
Lititz, PA 17543
Email: jmartin@emypeople.net

Edith Witmer
720 Church Rd.
Richfield, PA 17086
Email: daybreaktherapies@gmail.com

Carlisle Printing
OF WALNUT CREEK LTD
800.927.4196 · carlisleprinting.com
Sugarcreek, Ohio 44681

Dedication

Dedicated with love to my parents, Melvin and Miriam Martin, who have walked with me in my own neurological journey; whose love and devotion toward children have lighted the same fires in my own heart.

Introduction

I have had the privilege of knowing Joan over a long period of time. In my teen years, my family moved to Pennsylvania and began attending White Oak Mennonite Church, where Joan's family also attended. At that time I was seventeen, and Joan was eleven. I remember visiting her after she had been seriously burned. Even then, her attitudes were upbeat. Joan is a fighter.

Joan works as a neurophysiological therapist. The word *neurophysiological* is a big one, but its meaning is easy to understand. *Neuro* refers to the brain and the central nervous system, while *physiological* refers to the physical aspects of our bodies. Both must work together for development to occur in either system. The brain cannot develop normally without stimulation from the muscles and joints that facilitate movements in our bodies; and our bodies cannot develop without the support and commands that come from the brain.

Joan's life has been a beautiful unfolding of God's purpose for her, and the ministry of blessing God has been fulfilling through her, moves my heart to worship God. Thousands of children have come into Joan's program and walked out with changed lives. Recently I suggested to Joan that she should write what she has learned so that information can be preserved for the multitudes.

"I don't have time, Edith," she said. "Maybe you can do it for me." So we began the journey that has culminated in this book. We pray that God will further fulfill His purpose for Joan's life as you read these pages.

When we work with God in bringing healing to His people—especially children—we sense the heartbeat of God in ways that still our own small desires and endeavors, and lift us up where we begin to glimpse the panorama of life from God's point of view. It is then that we begin to share in the pathos of His heart when he says, *"Suffer little children, and forbid them not, to come unto me: for of such is the kingdom of heaven"* (Matthew 19:14). Joan has shared that call with God. Daily she lives with the knowledge that her life has an agenda that is not her own. Her heart is open to receive everyone God sends to her.

She also senses the battle within the spirit world that flares as Christ works through His ambassadors to redeem fallen mankind. *"For we wrestle not against flesh and blood, but against principalities, against powers, against the rulers of the darkness of this world, against spiritual wickedness in high places"* (Ephesians 6:12). Many of the clients Joan deals with are children. The devil does not want children to receive wholeness and healing, or to have minds that function well. Joan is mindful of the need to be covered daily by the blood of Jesus so that she will be protected and prepared to be a good soldier as she works in ministry with God. Pray for her.

Joan senses this spiritual warfare in the unusual accidents that have occurred in her life. One of these has been a life-altering automobile accident that took place in Spanish Lookout, Belize. Since that time, Joan has come to live with pain and limitation in a new way.

In her approach to her clients, Joan moves with a combination of assured confidence and gentleness. The impact of her carefully-chosen words is like soft butter as it melts into freshly-baked bread. Yet, if necessary, there is within her manner a firmness that is not unlike steel.

Jeremy, one of Joan's clients, understands this in the simplicity of his heart. As Jeremy and his family prepared for a trip to Pennsylvania to have an office visit with Joan, Jeremy told his mother, "I'm going to go running into Joan's office when we get there!"

"Why?" his mother asked.

"I can't wait to see Joan," he said. "I want to show her how good I am. Joan is firm. But Joan is kind. I just love Joan!"

Since I have become a neurophysiological therapist, I also enjoy Joan's world of ministry, and sharing notes with her. It is truly a delight to see the lives of individuals opening up with new vitality and purpose, like the petals of a dew-drenched flower under the rays of the morning sun. For it is the Sonlight of God that brings blessing and healing into the lives of children as God redeems fallen mankind. In heaven, that redemption will be complete. Until then, we battle with Him for the kingdom of God and the work of blessing the "little ones" He loves.

Considering that this book may be used as a reference source, we have overlapped some of the material in various chapters or sections. Joan and I have both contributed to this book. However, to avoid awkwardness, we have chosen not to identify the speaker. For efficiency, this book uses masculine gender pronouns to indicate common gender. We hope we have struck the right balance that will avoid confusion for our readers.

It has been a pleasure to share the writing of this book with Joan— and to reach out to you, the reader. If you wish to contact either of us, we welcome your response. You are free to use the contact information listed on page ii.

Sincerely,

–Edith Witmer

Contents

chapter one

Meet Joan...

I remember exactly how Janet looked.

I was eight at the time, and my family had traveled to Ontario to attend the Conservative Mennonite Fellowship Meetings. Our host family was caring for an 18-month-old foster child. When I first saw her, she was sitting on the living room floor, looking up at me with that adorable grin that only a Down's syndrome child can share.

I rushed to Janet and picked her up. Amazingly, she had no objections. For the remaining days of our visit, I was with Janet every available moment. Our attraction was mutual. I had fallen in love with the little girl, and she with me. And when I asked if we could take Janet along to church in our van, her mother agreed.

As we traveled south a few days later, my thoughts were full of Janet.

What could be better than having a special-needs sibling? I belonged to a God-fearing family who had taught me to pray. "Lord," I prayed with all the fervency of a little girl's cherished dream, "please send me a brother or sister just like Janet. I love Down's children!" It was the same prayer I would pray every night for many years.

My mother is a caring woman who nevertheless has a strong bearing of common sense. I did not share my prayer with her until I was grown. When I did, her eyes opened wide. "Joan!" she said, "nobody prays for handicapped children!" But I did.

In fact, I had many special-needs children in my fantasy world. As I grew up, I had no sisters who were close to my age. So I developed imaginative play. I had six sets of twins that I cared for every day. And one out of each set of twins was a Down's baby. Sometimes I fell asleep before I had mentally put all my children to bed.

I also embarrassed my siblings when we visited other people's homes. My eyes were drawn to bookshelves like magnets are to metal. And the moment I saw a book about learning disorders, handicaps, or any special needs—I took the book to our hostess and asked to borrow it.

The more I learned, the more I yearned to do something in the real world with handicapped children.

When I was eighteen, I heard about *Faith Mission Home* in Virginia. I thought it would be absolutely wonderful to relate to all the handicapped children there. I shared the thought with my parents and listed the glories of working there. They listened and pondered the question with me.

"Why don't you talk to our bishop?" My father finally said.

My bishop listened quietly while I shared my eager story with him. "I think you're a little young to do something like that now, Joan," he finally answered. "Why don't you teach school for a few years? There might even be a need for a special-ed teacher."

I was willing to work with that. So when I was almost twenty, I began teaching at Sporting Hill Mennonite School. I loved my third, fourth and fifth graders—and was fairly fulfilled. But I still longed for the handicapped children of my dreams.

I had been teaching school for five years when God sent two little angels to the White Oak Mennonite Church family, where I was a member. Kristopher Martin was a Down's syndrome baby, and Daniel Neuenschwander had macrocephaly hypotonia.

When Daniel was two years old, I was a dinner guest at the same place where his family had been invited. I watched Daniel struggling with blocks on the floor, only listening to half of the conversation in our ladies' circle. Finally I could wait no longer and slid onto the floor beside him. What a delightful time I had as I taught him how to put his blocks into the toy farm wagon.

The next day I received a call from his mother. "Joan," she said, "I noticed how well you worked with Daniel yesterday. I am so busy with all of my children. Would you mind working with Daniel a few days a week after school is out?"

"Do I have to wait that long?" I asked. It was only April. One and a half months of waiting seemed incredibly long.

Daniel's mother laughed. "Well, I don't know what you can handle. When would you like to start?"

So I began working with Daniel two afternoons a week, going to his house right after school. Eventually, I also began taking Daniel to his Easter Seals classes twice a week. I sat in on therapy sessions there, and helped with Daniel's therapy at his home. We continued with this pattern until Daniel was in school three years later.

The years were ticking past for me, and I still longed to work with handicapped children. I had only recently given my consent to teach at Sporting Hill for my eleventh year when a thunderbolt hit me.

"Joan." It was my mother's voice. "Did you know that Sporting Hill is looking for a special-ed teacher for Kristopher next year?"

I was chagrined. "What!" I exclaimed. "I've been waiting for an opportunity like this for ten years, Mom. And I just promised for another year in my regular classroom. How could I have missed this opportunity?"

Neither of us said much the rest of the evening, but when I got up in the morning, I knew what to do. I would go straight to the school board.

"I hear you're looking for a teacher for Kristopher," I began. "I would like to do it. It will be easier for you to find someone to teach a regular classroom than to find a special-ed teacher. Let me do it!"

No one said anything for a little. Then the chairman cleared his throat. "I don't think that's a good idea, Joan," he said. "After teaching normal children for ten years, you wouldn't want to teach in a special-needs classroom."

"Oh," I responded with enthusiasm, "but I do! I've been waiting for a chance like this."

After a bit of discussion, the chairman turned to me. "All right, Joan," he said, "we'll let you try it. But you'll find out it won't be much fun. We'll give you the chance to get your old classroom back after one year."

I was delighted, and Kristopher and I had a wonderful year.

It was January when two of the board members dropped into my classroom after school. The chairman cleared his throat. "We promised you the chance to get your old classroom back. We'd really rather you'd keep on working with Kristopher. But we're keeping our promise. If you want your old classroom back, you can have it."

"No," I said, as I looked about the room I shared with Kristopher and thought of the small milestones he was reaching, "I really can't think of anything I'd rather do than what I'm doing right now. Count me on board here with Kristopher."

I continued teaching special-ed for seven more years. During that time, my class grew larger. I searched for more ways to help my children, and moved into developmental testing. Eventually other schools and families learned about what I was doing, and requested my services. So my evenings and Saturdays were filled with appointments.

"Joan," my mother asked me, "are you sure you can keep on doing two jobs well?"

My mother was right. After some deliberation, I asked the school board for a year off so I could decide if I wanted to evaluate special-needs children or teach them.

The first summer after I stopped teaching special-ed, I went to Oregon to work with a special-needs child named Rose. I was able to be present while Svea Gold, a neurophysiological therapist, evaluated Rose.

I watched in amazement as Svea worked with the child. I had been praying for answers for my children—and here they were unfolding before my eyes! In thirty minutes, Svea had been able to diagnose the problem areas Rose encountered, and in the next fifteen, she told us what to do to help her.

Svea had been noticing my rapt attention and my amazement. "Is something wrong, Joan?" she asked me.

"No," I answered Svea. "I am simply amazed. I have never seen anyone do what you have done today. It's what I want to do myself. Where can I learn to do what you're doing?"

"Well," Svea smiled at me, "I'm going to be here in Oregon all summer, and so will you. If you're willing to work hard and come to me, I'll teach you what I know."

I was more than ready to work hard. And Svea, who was aging, looked upon me as the next person to carry the baton in her quest to help handicapped children. Svea did many things to increase my learning, and we shared phone time until her death.

So I went home from Oregon and began working as a neurophysiological therapist. And I have never looked back. In the eighteen years I have been in this work, God has answered my prayers many times over. God did not give me the Down's sibling I wanted. Instead, he has given me thousands of children whom I call mine.

It has been the deep joy of my heart to receive "little ones" whom Jesus loves, and to address the neurological problems that make their lives so difficult. As I work with them, their eyes begin to shine. Their balance improves. School work becomes easier. Their relationships with others blossom. Life opens up for them! And for their families… I ask for no greater joy in life than this.

Leonard came into my life when he was seventeen. I was almost at the point of discharging his sister on the completion of her program when his mother addressed me.

"Joan," she said, "Can you help Leonard?"

"How old is he?" I asked.

"Seventeen."

I pondered, and then shook my head. "How would you make a seventeen-year-old do exercises?"

"But he wants to," his mother persisted. "He sees the changes that have come into his sister's life. And he wants help."

It is my goal to help every person God sends to me. So I paused to pray. "God," I prayed, "what shall I do here?"

"All right," I said, "We'll give it a try."

I worked with Leonard for eighteen months. He transformed from an awkward young man who could not meet another person's eyes into a motivated, confident individual who had life before him. When I dismissed him, I looked into his face and saw the sparkle in his eyes. And I thanked God that I had not turned the young man away...

A few years had gone by when I heard the doorbell ring. I was surprised to find Leonard standing there.

"Joan," he said, as he handed me a bouquet of long-stemmed roses, "I wanted to thank you for saving my life."

I blinked. How had I saved his life? "I might have helped you, Leonard," I returned, "but I didn't save your life."

"Yes, Joan," he said as his voice became unsteady. "You did. If you had not been willing to work with me, I would have committed suicide."

After Leonard left, I sat down and simply cried. After all the prayers I had raised to God for answers for my children, what greater fulfillment could God have given me than to help bring life to yet another one of them?

chapter two

Food That Aids Development

My phone rang.

"Joan!" I recognized the voice of one of my clients. "Can you help me? I'm desperate!"

"I'd be glad to try, Elaine," I replied. "Can you tell me what's wrong?"

"It's Todd. You know he's two now. For the past two weeks, he's been going through a terrible stage with temper tantrums. Nothing works, and I don't know what to do anymore."

I could feel the tension oozing from the cell phone into my ear. I paused for a moment, thinking of the blue-eyed, flaxen-haired child with the lopsided smile, whom I had started seeing four months ago. What had gone wrong?

"Hmmm," I said, buying a bit of time. "Could you tell me a little about these temper tantrums, Elaine? When do they happen?"

"He usually starts acting up about 10:30 in the morning," Elaine answered. "Then he's all right after lunch until about the middle of the afternoon. He's happy again after supper. But then he gets really unreasonable by bedtime—when we're all tired."

A light flashed in my mind, and I thought of protein. "That sounds hard," I said. "But I think we have an easy answer. Could you tell me what he eats for breakfast?"

"Well," said Elaine, "he doesn't like eggs. So I give him dry cereal, usually Cheerios. He doesn't want milk on that either."

"I got that," I answered, as I jotted on my note pad. "Then what do you feed him for a mid-morning snack?"

"I don't give him a snack," Elaine answered. "We have a rule at our house that you only eat at mealtimes."

Ouch! I thought, as I recorded that one.

"And for lunch?" I asked.

"We usually have a vegetable, a complex starch, and something with protein. That's our main meal of the day."

"That sounds good," I answered. "And then nothing until suppertime?"

"That's right," she said. "For supper I'll have soup, leftovers, or whatever is available. But I try to do the protein, complex starch, vegetable thing again. But if supper is late, Todd really gets cranky!"

"What about a snack in the evening?"

"Nothing then either," Elaine said. "We feel that food at mealtimes is all the children need."

"I want you to try an experiment for me," I said, "and I think you'll soon have a happy boy."

"Really?" Relief flooded Elaine's voice. "I'll try anything you say, Joan. What is it?"

"I want you to decide what Todd eats for breakfast. Cut out all the refined sugars and starches. And give him lots of protein, complex carbs, and some fruits and vegetables. And milk from your cow."

There was a long pause. "Really?" Elaine returned, in a deflated voice. "You really mean… no boxed cereals? And just things like eggs, meat, milk, green beans from last night's supper, oatmeal, and that kind of thing?"

"Yes, Elaine," I replied. "The healthy things that will give Todd brain food. Then at ten o'clock, I want you to give Todd a protein snack. Something like a hard-boiled egg, a sandwich made from whole wheat bread and nut butter, or a piece of meat."

"All right," she said.

"Your lunches sound good," I continued. "Then give him another protein snack when he gets up from his nap in the afternoon. Give him another healthy supper, and then a protein snack before the time he gets cranky in the evening."

"That's about 8:00," Elaine said. "And you're sure this plan will work?"

"About ninety-five percent sure." I laughed. "You try that for two weeks and get back to me."

I sometimes thought of Todd in the next two weeks. And when Elaine called me back, I was all ears.

"How is it going, Elaine?" I asked.

"Really good," she said. "I've never had a happier little boy. But how did you know what was wrong, Joan? That's what my husband wants to know. He says we should do this all the time."

I stifled a laugh. "That's wonderful, Elaine. I'm very happy to hear that. It's just the way it works. Our brains can't work without fuel. And a child's stomach can't hold enough food to last for five hours. Now that you're giving Todd good fuel consistently, he's not trying to run on an empty tank. And that translates into a happy child."

❀ ❀ ❀

Have you experienced the sugar spikes that refined sugar and refined carbs create? After they are eaten, the resulting sugars rush into the bloodstream and create a high. So the body releases insulin to counter that—and emotional and physical energy levels fall flat again.

Proteins, on the other hand, are digested slowly, in a sustainable manner. The body breaks down protein to become brain food to last over a period of time. By providing protein at meals and snack times, we can avoid the highs and the lows that refined sugars and carbs create. Complex carbs also break down slowly, without overwhelming the body, and contribute to stable sugar levels, when eaten in moderate amounts.

Does the food we eat make a difference in our lives? In our abilities and vitality?

When we look at civilizations that have been healthy, and notice their eating habits, the answer to those questions stands out in black and white. And we see, as the saying goes, that we are what we eat.

Diets that are filled with empty calories and toxins create sickness and lethargy. People groups who eat real food, in correct proportions, have more vitality, energy and well-being. And their bodies heal faster.

Today we have little girls reaching puberty as early as eight or nine years old. Part of the reason for this probably comes in the meat and milk products they are eating, where hormones that are fed or injected into farm animals are passed along into the food they provide.

We understand that giving poor feed to our dairy herds will give them poor performance, and that defective fuel in our cars will create problems. Why does it take us by surprise when we learn that our own bodies work the same way?

Perhaps we live to eat, instead of eating to live. Food, by God's design, brings us pleasure and a sense of reward. And we love comfort foods that remind us of our mother's meals, or the satisfying taste of chocolate melting over our tongues. When we make selfish choices for instant pleasure, we sacrifice the real gift God placed in food.

What Should We Eat?

Starting with food that nourishes and heals is a very elementary step in helping our children develop healthy brains and bodies. To do that, it often becomes necessary to have our own little "Old MacDonald" farms, with a cow, some chickens, a few hogs and a huge garden—or to buy our food from farmers that honor organic practices. It is good to know the people who grow your food. Otherwise, it is difficult to know what actually went into producing them.

Since trans fats and food preservatives are necessary for a long shelf life, the simple answer to food sourcing is to stop buying prepared food at the grocery store—and make your own at home like your grandmother did. Research has also underscored that food colorings and preservatives increase brain distress that shows itself in neurological abnormalities. When food coloring and preservatives (which are necessary to prolong shelf life in the grocery stores) are taken out of children's diets, their neurological health improves.

Children have an even lower tolerance level for an unhealthy glucose load than adults do. This occurs when highly-refined sugars and carbs enter the bloodstream too quickly for the body to handle. Then children tend to have hypoglycemia-like symptoms, including shakiness and sweating, or being more easily distracted. Children tend to became agitated and uncooperative after they have binged on candy and cookies.

Cutting out all unhealthy sugars in the diet and using fruits, nuts and cheese for desserts gives a child healthy sugars and nutrients. Remember to give a child extra protein any time he has high amounts of healthy sugars, so he can process them well. Have hard-boiled eggs on hand for snack time.

We show our children what is good by what we model for them. When children are taught to eat wholesome food with gratitude, they enjoy those foods. Many people find that they no longer crave cheap junk foods after they have developed good eating habits.

There were very few food allergies in our grandparents' time. Only rarely were there neurologically-challenged children. People ate nutrient-dense food that left them with a satisfied feeling when they had eaten enough. They were generally healthy. And there was a great sense of reward from enjoying the food that came from the labors of their own hands. (For more information, see *Nourishing Traditions*, by Sally Fallon or search for information on The Weston A. Price Foundation.)

It pays to go chemical-free. Organophosphates are in the insecticides commonly used today in conventional chemical agricultural practices. These chemicals tamper with the nervous systems of bugs and critters— and are in the food that comes off these fields. They are present in the urine of children who eat conventionally grown food. What are these insecticides doing to the brains of our children?

MSG is another culprit found in processed foods. In 1908, a Japanese researcher found a new taste substance in seaweed kombu that was different from sweet, salty, sour and bitter. What he discovered was free glutamic acid. When you combine that with sodium, you have monosodium glutatate (MSG).

The discovery of MSG revolutionized the food industry. Using it, manufacturers could make food taste better at a very low cost. Moreover, by using MSG, they could obtain a taste that mimicked the taste of broth. So MSG became the critical ingredient in bouillon cubes and soup bases. It has many names and has been added to myriads of food items that taste good with cheap ingredients. MSG is a necessary ingredient to make high-fat, carbohydrate-rich, and high-sugar foods taste good. Most restaurants depend extensively on MSG to turn a profit.

So then, what is the problem with MSG? MSG damages the brain, particularly in young, developing children. Attacking the brain cells in the hypothalamus, MSG works havoc in hormones that are needed for growth, sleep, and the reproductive system. White flour foods contain cysteine, which causes the same problems MSG does. For a developing brain, even a short exposure to MSG and cysteine can bring about brain damage that results in learning disorders and bad behavior.

The food a mother eats today has long-range effects. When a little girl is born, she already carries the substance from which her eggs will be made. Those are gifted to her by her own mother. Therefore the health of her mother's body, and the foods that her mother ate, will affect several generations.

The gut of a child is sometimes called his second brain. Most of the serotonin the body produces is manufactured there. But if the gut has tiny holes that have been made by yeast and other problems, we see the condition that is called leaky gut. It is at the base of an entire system of problems that produce ill health. One of these is that the brain cannot function well if the condition is present, because it does not receive the nurture it needs.

This is why lacto-fermented foods and good probiotics are so essential. Good digestion is necessary for good health. Otherwise the food you eat cannot be absorbed by your body. You can provide good healthy flora for your gut by eating fermented foods. You can also take supplements that supply healthy flora. But if you use a supplemental form, make sure you have a quality product. If the flora you are trying to plant in your gut is dead by the time you swallow the capsule, it will not do you any good. A lot of the problems we see in children would not be present if their gut would have a happy balance of bacteria for digestion and health.

Our generation is rediscovering the wonderful treasure that comes from bone broth. Cooking meat and bones has been done for ages. When we use bone broth, we supply our body with multitudes of building blocks and healthful nutrients. Our children will have healthier bones, joints and skeletal systems if we use rich bone broths in our cooking. Today's children are much more at risk to bone fractures, as more and more boneless meats are being used. Chicken broth carries antibiotic properties as well. Comforting broths and stews that are made with bone broth help build healthier immune systems. (For more information, see *Nourishing Broth,* by Sally Fallon.)

Proteins Are Essential

We have already addressed this issue in the story at the beginning of this chapter. Protein provides the building blocks our bodies need to form and repair tissues, make hormones, and act to support many functions within our tremendously complex body systems. We all need protein at every meal, and for snacks.

16

What kind of protein should we eat? Since most protein found in grocery stores is produced with the use of hormones, it becomes important that we grow our own chemical-free meats, or know the source from which we are buying them. Grass-fed cows produce wholesome milk as well as wholesome meat. Ranged chickens produce much better eggs than those found on the grocery store shelves. Raw milk still contains the gifts God placed there for our use.

Good protein is highly essential for good brain function. In fact, our children cannot manage without it.

Use these snacks for good nutrition: cheese, meat, nuts, hard-boiled eggs, quality raw milk (A2A2 is best) and nut butters.

Good Fats are Fabulous!

In spite of the recent propaganda that fats need to be removed from our diets, healthy fats are good for you—even necessary. Good dietary fats supply your body with nutrients you cannot do without.

Essential fatty acids (those that your body cannot make) are often lacking in hyperactive children. Boys have a three times greater need for essential fatty acids than girls do. Dyslexia, dyspraxia, ADD and ADHD tend to run in families. This possibly indicates an inherited tendency to be deficient in essential fatty acids.

You will boost your child's brain power when you use Omega-3's and Omega-6's. Omega-3 is one of the fats that produce the myelin sheath that must cover the brain and nerves. They help messages pass quickly between brain cells to help us retain information and think clearly.

Omega-6 is found in the oils of grains and seeds, and in meat. It is important in forming the blood brain barrier, which keeps some drugs, chemicals and viruses from entering the brain. Omega-3 and Omega-6 keep brain cells from becoming brittle (which interferes with accurate work and slows thought processes). DHA helps the brain function with memory, speech and specific motor skills.

If you lack healthy fats, your body will not be able to absorb Vitamin D, a fat-soluble vitamin. You also need good fats to help transport Vitamins A, D, E and K into your bloodstream so that they can be absorbed. Vitamin A is important for vision and skin. You need Vitamin D for good bone health, and Vitamin E contributes to cellular function. Vitamin K is needed for blood clotting.

Without good fats, your body cannot absorb any of these. For example, Vitamin K is found in leafy greens. But unless you eat them with some fat, your body will not be able to absorb the Vitamin K. This is why a green salad should be accompanied with olive oil, nuts, seeds or cheeses.

On the other hand, trans fats, manufactured to prolong grocery store shelf life, clog your vessels and confuse your body. We should also avoid all oils and fats that are produced from GMO sources. Then bring animal fats from animals raised without steroids and hormones into your diet. Use coconut oil, olive oil, and other healthy oils as you prepare meals. Your body will thank you for the difference.

Our brains are about 60 percent fat, made of fats like Omega-3 that must be obtained from diet. This is why a mother should take plenty of Omega-3's as her baby's brain and nervous systems develop during pregnancy. God put a lot of DHA, a long-chain fatty acid, in human breast milk. But when a child fails to get enough DHA, his brain does not develop as well.

Studies have shown that people who eat fish regularly do better on memory tests, psychomotor speed, cognitive flexibility and overall cognitive ability. (EPA and DHA are specific activators for this.) Eating fish also decreases the risk of Alzheimer's and dementia. We find good DHA sources in fatty fish such as mackerel, lake trout, herring, sardines, albacore tuna and salmon.

Our diets interact with our genes to determine how quickly and to what extent plaques build up in the passages of our brains. Good brain function is produced when signals move smoothly between brain cells. As we give our bodies fresh supplies of fatty acids, these connections are refreshed.

Fish oils feed the brain. Evening primrose oil nurtures the nervous system. Eating healthy fats promotes good mental health and happier moods. Powerful fatty acids help nerve cells communicate more effectively. That means that brain chemicals that promote a feeling of wholeness, like serotonin and dopamine, can move in and out of the brain cells with more ease. When this is happening, our moods are more positive and productive. There is also increasing evidence that Omega-3 helps psychotic and bipolar disorders.

I remember Alex, a struggling four-year-old, who entered my program. I recommended that the mother put him on primrose oil, fish oil and bone broth. In three months' time, his mother was delighted and amazed to see a tremendous change in her son—because his mind and body had received the needed nutrients to heal and build. Most things in life are truly simple.

Underscore this in your memory—coconut oil, olive oil, butter and animal fats from healthy animals are all good fats that enhance brain health. Avoid all hydrogenated fats and oils, including margarine, since these synthetic fats poison our body systems and create sluggish brains.

Remember Iron!

Iron is an important mineral for children. Red meat, especially liver, is the richest source of iron, though it is also found in lentils, red beets, beans, nuts and seeds. Iron works together with proteins in the bone marrow, where hemoglobin is produced. The job of hemoglobin, then, is to carry oxygen to the brain and other body tissues. Oxygen is very important for brain function, and for all body tissues at the cellular level. Lack of iron produces small red blood cells that carry small loads of hemoglobin.

Children with ADHD tend to have low iron levels. In one study, eighty-four percent of ADHD children had low iron levels. The lower the level, the more troubled the child was with hyperactivity, low cognitive function and oppositional behaviors. However, none of these children would have been called anemic by the medical critique. When these researchers fed appropriate iron sources to ADHD children, they improved.

Lack of iron is probably affecting our children's attention spans, as well as their ability to focus and concentrate.

Eat Lots of Fruits and Vegetables

Fruits and vegetables carry payloads of good nutrition and create variety in a healthy diet. Raw and cooked greens boost brain power. Lightly steamed vegetables are best for children. Cup for cup, broccoli has more calcium than milk does.

Choose ripe vegetables. Green peppers, for example, are actually immature and are therefore harder to digest. This is why they produce more belching than yellow and red peppers.

While some raw foods are good for adults, do not feed children raw foods until they have teeth and their digestive systems can handle them. I like to see a baby given some raw food in his high chair to play with, but not too much.

Fruit juices are not ideal for children because they can cause sugar spikes. It is best to eat the fruit whole, so that the fibers and enzymes that are needed to handle the sugar are present. Remember that we handle fruits better when they are eaten with some protein to help stabilize blood sugars.

It is important that the fruits and vegetables you use are not contaminated with insecticides and herbicides, and are not grown from GMO seeds. You are blessed if you are able to buy all of your fruits and vegetables from local or organic growers. A number of websites keep viewers posted on which fruits and vegetables are most likely to be contaminated. If you cannot buy what you need from trustworthy sources, the food on these lists are the most important ones to avoid.

Dealing With Food Allergies

If we wait to introduce high-allergen foods to children until they are two years old, we will have fewer resulting food allergies. In this group I am including gluten, as well as dairy, corn and eggs that come from grocery store shelves. Since they have been so corrupted, the child's body does not know how to handle the alien substances, and is likely to develop one of the food sensitivities that has become rampant today. I have found that the Gut and Psychology Syndrome (GAPS) diet is great for working with food sensitivities and digestive issues.

We also find that a lot of children who have neurological problems have food sensitivities. The two conditions go hand in hand. We are not sure which one comes first. About 60 percent of the children I see in my office arrive with food allergies. I see the diagnosis written on their faces when I see pale, pasty skin and puffiness under their eyes. When we are able to bring healing to the brain with neurophysiological therapy, eighty percent of the children lose their food allergies. While we are not entirely sure why this occurs, we know that the immune system headquarters are located within the brain.

Handling Seizures

When we are dealing with seizures, I advise parents of children to provide protein between every meal and at bedtime. This, as well as removing all sugar, makes a difference for many people. Seizures are also directly related to constipation. Putting a child on a no-carb diet will help to address this.

When we take away sugar, carbs, and preservatives, and supply tons of good fats, our seizure-oriented children usually improve.

Other Common Sense Factors That Foster Mental Health

Encourage children to exercise—to run, jump and play with abandon! When children exercise, they generate new brain cells in the hippocampus, cells that work with memory. Physical exercise also increases the chemical messages that flash between the hippocampus and the front part of the brain. These messages help us with cognitive functions such as reasoning, perceiving ideas, solving problems, calculating problems and comparing issues.

Children should play outside. We all need natural sunlight to stimulate Vitamin D so we can have healthy bones. Sunlight also helps us be alert, supports good moods, and fosters good behaviors. And when children play outside, they inhale fresh air, which has about four thousand negative ions per cubic centimeter. These negative ions in the composition of the air particles produce hormonal and chemical reactions in the body and brain, which helps to produce feelings of well-being and good health. When your child becomes irritable, remember to send him outside for some vigorous play. Swinging, riding bike, or just running provides wonderful developmental therapy. Most children need some vigorous exercise after they come home from school.

Water is very important for all of our body tissues. A two percent drop is enough to cause some short-term memory loss, make it difficult to think clearly, and leave us feeling fatigued. So help your children drink lots of water—and their concentration, good moods, reasoning and behavior may improve by twenty-five percent. For nonverbal or young children, make water easily accessible. Or remember to offer a drink frequently.

Put your children to bed early. Without adequate rest, our brains cannot repair themselves for the next day. Lack of sleep leads to sloppy decisions, poor cognition, and unnecessary accidents. Studies show that you can lose three percent of your IQ for each short night. Do that five days in a row, and you may be operating on eighty-five percent of the IQ ability you could have with healthy sleep habits.

And don't forget a good breakfast. Breakfast wakes up a child's metabolism and recharges the brain with energy for another day. Children who are not given breakfast cannot perform adequately in school. Breakfast needs to include good protein such as eggs, meat, or nut butter on wholesome toast. If your child has trouble digesting food early in the morning, try a protein shake.

※ ※ ※

Avoid These...

It is best not to give peanut butter to a child before he is three years old. He is less likely to develop a sensitivity at that point.

All artificial food coloring is hazardous to your health. The worst of these are red, yellow and orange food coloring. Artificial food preservatives are also an unhealthy choice, and are found in nearly all commercially produced foods.

Caffeine is not healthy for our children. Black and green teas contain caffeine. While herbal teas are good for babies and children, remember that some mint teas contain caffeine as well.

Gluten, an inflammatory food, dulls the brain and clogs the digestive system. However, the gluten-free foods you can buy at your local grocery store are not a good option either. They often contain high percentages of starches, as well as unhealthy preservatives. Instead, learn to make your own.

While dark chocolate has some health advantages for adults, hyper children generally cannot handle it. One of my clients, a small boy, was given a small piece of chocolate candy by a relative, and bounced off the walls for two hours afterward.

Too many starches, particularly those processed from GMO sources, make children chunky and slow. Carbohydrates are also addicting.

At seven years old, Patrick was twenty-five pounds overweight. He moved with an unnatural, stiff shuffle. After we started him on exercises, his mother decided to put him on a low-carb diet. As his coordination improved, he also dropped pounds. And he could think better. When the day arrived that he caught his first high pop, he was delighted. So were we!

When we take all refined food, including white sugar and white flour, artificial coloring and preservatives out of the diets of hyperactive children—they improve greatly! For eating those items causes inflammation in the brain. Some parents say that only removing these toxins causes their sons and daughters to become different children.

Good food is a reward and a blessing. When we make healthy food choices, we reach out to receive gifts that will foster healthy minds and bodies and that will help us to be good stewards of the temples God has given us.

Following is a quick checklist of nutrients that build brain function.

Choline for good memory.
Choline is found in eggs and nuts. Scramble eggs over cooked vegetables, and eat a slice of whole grain bread slathered with good butter.

Antioxidants for memory improvement.
Many foods provide brain-boosting antioxidants like Vitamins A, C and E. Use fresh fruit and vegetables at meal times and for snacks. Prepare hummus and use as a dip for raw veggies. Make smoothies with kefir or yogurt bases. Add fruits and protein powders. These are also great for after-school snacks.

Omega-3 fatty acids for cognitive functions.
If you want to be able to think well, eat plenty of fish, like salmon or mackerel.

Fish cakes provide us with a very healthy protein snack. Avocados, flaxseed products, nuts, and extra-virgin olive oil offer more good possibilities for our diets. Avocados can be eaten out of the shell, made into guacamole, sliced into sandwiches, or put into smoothies. Olive oil can be used in salad dressings, in flavored dipping oils and so on. To get the most from your extra-virgin olive oil, do not heat it.

Whole grains to improve your memory function.

Whole grains are complex carbs whose folate and other B vitamins boost memory function. They contain fiber, which your digestive tract needs, and provide energy over an extended period of time.

Cook old-fashioned oatmeal with Celtic salt, top with fresh or frozen berries, drizzle with maple syrup—and then add A2A2 organic milk. Delicious and nutritious!

Iron for mental alertness.

Iron improves both mental function and energy levels. Eat red meat, poultry, spinach, raisins, beans, and whole grains. Make a trail mix with dried fruit, nuts, and a whole grain product. A fourth cup makes a serving.

Calcium for strong bones.

Calcium builds strong bones and teeth, and helps children be physically active. Check to see what the daily requirement is for the age of your child.

Make wholesome dairy products from raw milk: kefir, yogurt, and cheese. Or enjoy a glass of cold raw milk produced by grass-fed cows. Almonds, salmon and tofu also supply calcium. Or make meat (unprocessed) and cheese roll ups.

Drink lots of water!

Maintaining hydration prevents fatigue and aids concentration. Drop sodas and sugary drinks. Most of the time we should be drinking plain water. For a little sprite, add a slice of lemon, lime or orange to your water. Herbal teas come in as a good second choice.

These foods will drain your mental resources:

- Foods with artificial sweeteners or coloring

- High fructose corn syrup

- Sugary fruit drinks, colas and juices

- Refined white sugars and breads

- Trans fats and partially hydrogenated oils

- Processed snack foods and luncheon meats

Fat Facts

· Essential fatty acids compose the membranes of each cell. The brain requires large volumes of fats.

· Sixty percent of the brain is composed of fats; of these fats, 30 percent is DHA, a long-chain fatty acid.

· Brain synapses need long-chain fatty acids to work well.

· DHA is needed in the rods of the retina to see well in the dark and to adjust to bright lights.

· The forebrain has the highest concentration of DHA.

· DHA is necessary for fetal and infant brain development.

· Children with milk intolerance sometimes have a deficiency in essential fatty acids.

· Children with poor motor skills and coordination often lack essential fatty acids.

Five Toxins That Muddle Children's Brains

· Gluten

· Artificial Sweeteners

· MSG

· Refined Sugar

· Fluoride

chapter three

Building Healthy Emotions

Jennie wipes her hands and turns to the crying baby. Tenderly she picks up Sharon and kisses her soft cheek. Like rose petals... Is it possible that it has been only two weeks since Sharon has joined the household? This tiny girl is now such an integral part of her life that it is hard to imagine what life was like without her.

"Are you a hungry girl?" Jennie croons softly, as she settles into the recliner and prepares to nurse the baby. Sharon quickly latches on and begins to fill her tummy with milk, making little slurping noises. Jennie's eyes shine warmly as she watches the face of the child she holds so closely in her arms. This treasure… this gift from God.

"I love you, Sharon," Jennie speaks softly, as she brushes a wisp of hair from the small forehead. "You are a gift from God."

At the sound of Jennie's voice, Sharon's eyes open and catch the sparkle in her mother's eyes. Then again she turns her full attention to nursing. But after a minute her eyes search for her mother's face again. Jennie smiles and holds her gaze.

"Such a sweet baby," she murmurs tenderly, as she kisses the top of Sharon's head.

What is taking place as Jennie nurses her child? Yes, Sharon is receiving life-giving nourishment. But that is only a portion of the moment she is sharing with her mother. For in the close sharing, their spirits are bonding. This is prime relationship time. As her oxytocin flows, Jennie's heart is full and running over with tender joy. She relaxes. And Sharon settles comfortably in her arms, knowing that all of the things she innately desires are being met. She is receiving food. And she is in total comfort as the unconditional love of her mother surrounds her physically and emotionally. Her inner person is nurtured every time Jennie meets her eyes with a warm sparkle in her own.

The desire to experience joy in loving relationships is the strongest motivation a child knows in the first two years of his life. Joy comes through upbuilding relationships. And children look forward to again finding joy—by being with their loved ones.

We will always seek joy because God created our hearts to serve and have fellowship with Him. The essence of joy is found in relationships. The path to joy opens to us when someone is delighted to be with us, and we thrive in the glow of their gift to us. God created us with brains that function best when joy is in charge. Therefore we reach for relationships that will lead us to joy.

Imagine that a child is running to someone who is waiting to receive him with open arms in unrestrained joy—and ponder the incredible gift that we give our loved ones when our total communication says, "I am so glad to see you!"

Neuroscience tells us that there is an area of the brain, located in the right, orbital pre-frontal cortex, that never loses its capacity to grow, as other parts of the brain do. It is this part of the brain that stores joy and builds emotional stability, that gives us the emotional resilience to return to joy after pain.

This area of the brain is also the bonding region. The security and strength a child develops as his parents nurture him depends both on the amount and timing of the gifts of joy he receives.

This "joy center" of the brain will have executive control over an individual's emotional system for his lifetime. Closely connected here is the ability to trust others that is developed as a child bonds with his parents—and finds that it is safe to do so.

As children know that their family members are "glad to be with them," they are able to live in an atmosphere of joy and to learn that joy should be the normal state in which we live. And their worlds become whole, when they know that there will be a way back to joy after they have had unpleasant experiences.

The baby's bond with his mother becomes the most important foundation for his emotional and neurological stability. The bond that a child forms with his mother begins the moment after he has been conceived. Unborn babies know whether or not they are wanted and if their mothers are anxious or at peace. By the time a child is born, he has been in tune with his mother for nine months. At that point, the bond is nearing completion, and within a few weeks it should be largely established. For this reason, nearly all of the newborn's care should come from his mother. Outside of the home, it is better not to allow others to hold him freely during this time period.

The mother should be the only one to feed the baby for the first five to six months of his life, even if he is being bottle fed. Feeding the baby provides a wonderful bonding opportunity. For this reason, even the father should find other ways to share in the baby's life.

The bond with the father is also important. However, it should become established secondarily to the bond the newborn develops with his mother. Notice that by the design of pregnancy and feeding the child, God arranged that babies and mothers should be inseparable.

The prime window for bonding continues until the child is about two years old. Mothers and babies belong together, and mothers are wise when they rarely leave their babies with sitters. I am always glad when mothers bring their babies along with them when they bring an older child to me for evaluation.

For those mothers who are not able to nurse their children, remember that you can sit down and spend dedicated time with your baby as you bottle-feed him. Remember to switch your child's head position from your right arm to your left arm alternately. This will help his eyes develop normally. Do not give this time to other family members. You can smile into his eyes, and treasure the child you hold in your arms—and in your heart. And you will both experience bonding.

As you interact with your children, remember these pointers:

- Smile when you meet each family member. Use sincere voice tones. Ask questions that invite others to honestly share how they are doing.

- Truly care about the person, understanding his fears, joys, passions, talents and pain. Treat everyone in your life with dignity and respect.

- Use touch appropriately. The gift of a hand placed on the shoulder, a heartfelt squeeze, and a kiss on the cheek convey volumes. Without it, children fail to develop optimally. Children cannot develop normally without the gift of touch.

- Find out what brings joy to your child. Do those things with him. Find little surprises that will make your child's eyes light up. And let your own eyes shine as you give the gift. Remember that joy in the relationship builds up as glances go back and forth.

- Cherish your babies and children, showing with your words and actions that you truly are "glad to be with them."

Babies enter the world totally helpless, waiting to be loved and cared for. As we share the love of Christ in our hearts with them, we are able to give them the gifts that will make their hearts glow.

It is the supreme gift of parenthood to share the love of God in a way that will help our children to understand their heavenly Father's love. God has set His heart upon us. *"Since thou wast precious in my sight, thou hast been honorable, and I have loved thee:..."* (Isaiah 43:4). How precious is the love of God! May we share that love with the little ones He has given us!

❊ ❊ ❊

The children God has placed in our care should learn to know who they are, and eventually what their purpose is in life. We form our children's mental concepts of who they are by our world view, and by the way we view and treat them.

The only correct way for a man to see himself is as a created being whose purpose is to love, worship and serve God. Understanding this keeps us from putting either ourselves or our children at the center point of our lives. We teach this God-fearing attitude indirectly in the first years of our children's lives. As we read Bible stories and teach them to know the heart of the Father, Whom we love, we also teach them directly.

As we relate to our children, it is important to continually remind them that they are treasures by relating to them with loving, unconditional acceptance. This forms their personal identity. It is important that we work with our children in a way that they unconsciously learn a sense of God and His purposes, and how we can please God. Otherwise they will see themselves at the center of a self-centered existence. Without these gifts that come from strong relationships, they will tend to long for joy without knowing how to achieve it, and instead cycle around the pain in their lives.

Belonging to a family gives us strong roots that blossom out into all other relationships. When we know that we "belong" simply because we have been born into our families, that we are loved, cherished and needed, our hearts thrive. We learn to give and take and to handle the traumas of life. We know there will always be a safe place to come back to as we meet the demands and experiences of life.

I think of Ian, a second grader with a pinched face. "Sister Edith," he would say as he came to my desk before school, "Do you know what we did last night?" So I would lay aside my red pen and smile into the hungry eyes that were trying to absorb all of me. Somewhere between the tale of the new kittens and the one about his bike accident, he would begin to relax. And sometimes he would reach out and touch my hand. Eventually he would sigh a good kind of sigh, give me a smile, and go out to play with the other children. His emotional "battery" had been recharged enough to start the day.

It is important that children find someone in their lives who will validate and nurture them. Our children will find it difficult to know how to give and receive in a positive way unless they have first sensed the love and acceptance of Christ in the person of someone within their community.

We can hurt our children in two ways. There is the heart cry of children who have never been given the birthright God has intended that every child should receive from his parents. The second way children are hurt lies in selfish, sinful acts that are done against them that damage and hurt their hearts and bodies. Children who have been wounded experience feelings of rejection, shame, fear, abandonment, humiliation and guilt.

As adults, we move toward maturity when we are comfortable seeing and acknowledging events as they really are. Life is often filled with pain and disappointment. Promises are broken and dreams die. When we no longer struggle with our acceptance of sorrow, we are ready to reach out to Christ who was wounded for our transgressions, and by whose stripes we are healed (Isaiah 53:5). Honesty makes us touchable and brings us to the threshold of finding healing. We show our wholeness, or maturity, by the way we relate to others in giving and receiving, and the ways in which we handle loss and disappointment. Do we make competent, selfless contributions to the lives of the people we touch? Or are we continually controlling and draining other people to accomplish our own agendas? Can we retain calm control and poise in the middle of difficulties—or do we fly apart when trouble comes?

In the same way as a sponge absorbs water, children learn these lessons by watching the way their parents live. They also develop their own index about the way they view themselves, and their sense of worth and competence by the way they see us viewing them. How do you handle the mistakes your children make? Are you shocked? How do you respond when they come to you with a small hurt? And how do you respond when they have been successful?

It is important to listen to the problem your child brings. Help him to express the struggle and pain he is experiencing. When he puts his feelings into words, he will be better able to understand and deal with them. Then move on to a solution in an honest, caring, logical manner. If your world is not upset by the problems your children bring to you, they learn that neither is theirs. They see that probably they are going to be all right.

We rob our children of security if we fail to be in authority over them.

A child who is in control is a very unhappy child who looks for someone who will give him boundaries. Good parenting involves a strong union of love, discipline and accountability. It is difficult for a child to develop in a healthy neurological pattern without all of these.

A child will not feel secure unless his parent holds him accountable to obedience. This begins at a very young age, when the command "Come" is given. It continues throughout the adolescent and teenage years, when the developing individual is still held accountable for his actions.

Parenting requires strong doses of common sense. Combine firmness and gentleness as you work with your child. Be understanding, yet matter-of-fact. Only as you understand self-discipline and personal responsibility will you be able to teach those same concepts to your child.

Remember to let your children be children. Maturity is not something that can happen in a day, a week, or a year. A parent leads his child in a wholesome manner when he is reasonable in what he expects the child to do. It is true that children need to learn to be quiet and still. However, a child's predominant need is to have plenty of physical outlets where he can run, jump, skip and hop. This allows him to work off his energy and aids his body and mind in healthy development.

Instead of keeping a struggling child in from recess to finish a lesson, a wise teacher will find other methods. He will also let the same child go outside for a five-minute vigorous swing ride or a run around the school building between recesses. This will rejuvenate the child's mind.

MATURITY LEVELS IN CHILDHOOD

Infant (Birth to Three Years)
A baby enters the world as a completely helpless individual who depends on others to do necessary things for him. It is important that he receives unconditional loving care. A baby innately knows that he is

receiving love when he is fed and tenderly cared for by his parents. We have talked about the sparkle in the eye that develops the infant's joy center. As a child is fed, dried, kissed and held tenderly when he cries, he is learning to give. As children sense that they are welcomed and loved, they grow the "joy center" in the right frontal cortex.

As an infant grows older, he learns that he can return to joy after feeling upset; this forms the basis for his sense of security. He knows that though trouble may come, everything will be all right again. As the infant sees loving faces and receives gentle handling, trust and bonding take place. This basic sense of security will go with the child for the rest of his years.

Child (Four to Twelve)

When a boy or a girl can describe and make requests for his welfare, he or she passes into the child stage. This is the beginning of taking responsibility for himself. As the years pass, he becomes more and more capable of doing tasks that make it possible for him to care for himself. It is still very important that he receives unconditional love and acceptance from his parents and community.

In this stage, it is important that he learn what brings him personal satisfaction, and to do hard things. He will need guidance as he perseveres in learning this. He should also recognize the gifts and resources that are uniquely his, and learn to use them well as he builds a life of personal meaning and purpose.

It is important that we help our children understand themselves, and that we teach them to share that information with others. Being able to put words to our feelings is an important step in being honest with ourselves and handling our emotions well.

The "entitlement" trend in our society, which suggests that we are owed a good life without our effort, tends to affect the way we look at personal responsibility. We do our children a grave wrong when we rob them of the opportunity to learn gratitude, accountability and responsibility. Without understanding these important principles, a child will become stuck on his road to maturity.

At this stage, children are beginning to see how they fit into the whole picture of life, both past and present. Knowing this will help them to find their way in the future.

Developing Adult (Thirteen to Twenty)

You will know that your child is reaching this developmental level when he is able to think about more than himself and his own desires. Previously he was learning to care for himself. Now he develops the ability not only to care for himself but also to contribute to others.

Identifying with a group and bonding with peers is an important task for this period. Personal growth develops as the individual is able to impact life around him and enjoy the rewards of success. He also learns to search for truth and fairness in his life community. This is very important as the developing individual learns that life is bigger than himself.

During this stage the individual learns to remain emotionally stable in disappointments or difficult situations. He also learns to find his own way back to joy after sorrow, and to help others do the same.

Another important task to accomplish in this time period is to develop his inner person, receiving and refining the gifts God has given him with joy. He will experience passion, pain, and purpose—further defining who he really is. The more he can realize and express these deep values, the more he will be able to live truthfully.

❊❊ ❊❊ ❊❊

In order for us to understand the emotional and physical needs of our children, it is imperative that we start with the fear of God in our hearts. We should have a proper understanding of what the word need really means. Most people who write and counsel, considering themselves able to practice as Christian psychologists, are using little more than poorly veiled modern psychology—where they see man as a little god, competent in himself, in the center of things.

While there are many theoretical views, in a generalized way modern psychology promotes the idea that a baby is born either as a good or a neutral being. If his needs are met and his "love tank" is filled, he will be able to become a competent individual who thinks well of himself and is therefore happy. He will probably make worthwhile contributions to his society. But if his needs are not met, and he becomes a man who does foolish or socially unacceptable things, he is not personally responsible for the way he acts. Life has shaped who he has become. In that case he suffers from a disease. Man is expected to live for his personal satisfaction. Sin is not recognized. Modern psychology begins and ends with man, apart from God, and denies that the cross exists. It sees truth as relative, and man as a puppet who cannot rise higher than the support he receives in his lifetime.

When we have a Biblical understanding of our place in life before God, we accept the fact that we have a carnal nature that must repent before we can be in harmony with our heavenly Father. From that point our lives are dependent upon God, and we worship Him, knowing Him and honoring Him with our obedience. We learn to think God's thoughts and humbly act upon the truth. God is at the center of our lives. Then grace will flow into our lives with harmony and blessing. And our actions will honor the God who first created and then redeemed us.

A Biblical understanding of man begins and remains with God at the center. Its focus is the cross. While we are blessed when others gift our lives with positive investments, the Bible teaches us that we are responsible to make good choices in the ways we think and act. With God, we are able to respond to our circumstances in a building, God-honoring way that God will use for His glory and our blessing.

It is imperative that we teach our children that they are not victims unable to rise above the circumstances of their past or present. Teach them to live humbly, honestly—basing their lives on choices rather than feelings.

As we help our children, we must teach them to be God-oriented— which will make all the difference in the directions their lives go, for now and for eternity.

⁂ ⁂ ⁂

A good family schedule creates a sense of healthy order in a child's life. Children do better when they know when to get up, when to do their chores, at what time to eat breakfast, and when to go to bed again at night. It becomes one of the means of teaching our children to live with a sense of self-discipline, meaning and purpose. Normal routines help to create a sense of security for children who are dealing with neurological problems and find it difficult to cope well with change. This way, something is the same every day. And they can use their limited resources for solving other problems.

Adequate sleep is essential if we want our children to be able to handle life well. It is while we sleep that the body repairs and refreshes itself. An infant needs fourteen to eighteen hours of sleep within a twenty-four hour period. Toddlers should have from twelve to fifteen. For growing children, we should allow for ten to twelve-hour nights.

Children are secure when they know that their parents love each other. Love, respect and consideration are learned as a child observes the way his parents relate to one another and society in general. This also forms the foundation of learning to respect and appreciate his own personhood.

Handle family activities in a way that builds a sense of community and sharing. We want to create a sense of belonging in our children that is built upon being a part of a larger group, a "we" group. As we teach and allow our children to make contributions in family group settings, they learn that they can do things well—and that they are needed. And their sense of personal worth and confidence grows. This forms a necessary part of learning to give and receive. Our children need to learn that life does not cycle around them, and that they are here to fit into the broader picture.

It is important that we share our own lives and experiences with our children. Encourage your child to talk about his life to you. Be ready to stop what you are doing and listen. Use body language and words that convey the message that you love your children unconditionally, and that you will help and support them in any situation they need to work through, even when they have done wrong. God does this for us as we develop. A parent represents God to his children.

Pay attention to a child's small hurts and sorrows. When Johnny knocks his elbow and comes to you, kiss his elbow. Tell him, "I'm sorry you got hurt, Johnny. It's all right to cry. But tell me about what happened." As we listen and gently apply Band-Aids, children know that they have found a safe refuge. They learn that life is, after all, a safe place to be. Then we move cheerfully on with life, and they learn that after sorrow, they can return to joy.

It is also important that we let children talk about negative emotions. Let your child share with you the anger he is feeling. Then help him look at the problem in a logical way, and look for a God-honoring solution. In this way, your child will learn to cope with life and to heal from its rough spots. A child feels safe again when he knows he has been "heard" by his parent. Someone knows him, loves him, sees who he really is—and is helping him through.

Share a life of delight and wonder with your son or daughter. Ponder the miracle of a tiny kitten, the glory of a sunset, the intrigue of an earthworm. Encourage your sons and daughters to explore the wonderful gift of childhood, to be curious, ask questions, and explore. And to develop creativity.

Shannon has learned that it works best to check eight-year-old Jeremy's trouser pockets before she throws the trousers into the washer. Then she saves the contents and discusses them with Jeremy. In this way she has learned that the best place to find interesting bugs is beside the garden water faucet. She has learned about the sparrow's nest in the spruce tree. Once when she and Jeremy went out to watch the nest quietly for ten minutes, they arrived in time to see the young birds fledge. They will always treasure the sheer delight of the shared moment.

Approach whatever happens with a positive attitude. Your child will learn to live the same way. Don't allow what you "think other people think" about you and your child to embarrass you. Let your child live freely and happily in what is appropriate for his age group.   Build up your child with sincere, honest compliments.

Sadie remembers the glow she felt at the end of a hard day, a glow that made any effort worthwhile, when her father smiled and said, "You have done a wonderful job, Sadie. I am very pleased." And the glow still remains in her heart. Now she longs for the day when her heavenly Father will say, *"Well done, thou good and faithful servant...enter thou into the joy of thy Lord"* (Matthew 25:21).

Parents mirror the heart of God for their sons and daughters.

※ ※ ※

Learn what kind of gift makes your child's heart grow. Some children love small, tangible gifts. Others thrive on one-on-one time spent together, or on acts of service that are done for them. For some children, words of affirmation are the supreme gift. Appropriate physical touch is the greatest gift to others.

A good way to find the best gateway to your child's heart is for the mother to ask the question, "What does Daddy do that tells you he loves you, Cheryl?" Or the father can ask the same question about the inputs the child cherishes from his mother. The answer to that question will help you to learn how you can make meaningful deposits in your child's life.

Eric, a third grader, stumbled through the hard knocks of life, running into many unnecessary problems. His teacher was punishing him three or four times a week. And his parents often needed to punish him at home.

"What is wrong, Joan?" Eric's father asked me. "Things aren't coming together, and we're all frustrated."

"I see what you're saying," I replied. "You have a frustrated child, a lot of discipline—and things still aren't working. What can you do that makes Eric feel loved?"

"We'll find out," his father replied.

That evening, he and Eric took a walk as they checked the electric fence. After a bit of small talk, Eric's father stopped and smiled into the boy's eyes. "I am wondering about something, Eric," he said. "If I could do something for you that would make you really happy, what would it be?"

Eric's eyes glowed as he pondered his huge opportunity. Then his face broke into a smile. "Would you pack my lunch, Dad? I would love that."

So Eric's father began packing his son's school lunch box each morning before he left for work. Sometimes he would write a note on the napkin, put a gummy worm inside a peanut butter-filled apple, or draw a smiling face on a banana.

"How is school going for Eric?" his father asked the teacher a week later.

"Wonderful!" the teacher exclaimed. "What did you do to Eric? He is so good. And you should see how happy he is at lunch time. He has a huge grin on his face, and for some reason he is one of the last ones done eating now. And he hasn't acted out all week."

Eric's family built on what they were learning about their son. When his mother was ready to put his mended clean clothes back into the dresser drawer, she showed them to him. "I did this for you, Eric," she said. "I washed your shirts and sewed a missing button on for you. I love to take care of you." And Eric thrived because a missing link had been filled in his heart.

Learn what matters to your child, and share those moments with him. The things that bring affirmation, rest and security to one child will vary from that of another. Until the child is three, focus equally on different kinds of gifting. After that, the child may develop his own preferences. God has made each of us individuals, uniquely created to fill a spot that only we can fill.

✺ ✺ ✺

You will not be able to build healthy emotions in your child unless you accept him the way he is. Parents often create burdens in the lives of their children because they themselves have unmet expectations that they hope their child will fill for them. When we as parents cease to struggle with these unmet goals, and when we are willing to be human—half of the battle has been won. Then, instead of depending on our children to establish our identity, we are ready to move actively into caring for them. Unless our children know that we love and accept them as they are, they will not feel comfortable with us.

Grace has moved through her life trying to be someone she isn't. She was number seven in a family that already had six girls. Her father, a farmer, was hoping desperately for a son to replace the hired man and become the next generation to carry on the tradition of the family farm. His face fell when he saw the tiny baby nursing in his wife's arms. Another girl! As Grace was growing up, she tried very hard to please her father. Maybe he would like her if she learned to whistle? To lift heavy feed bags? Today, Grace is always trying to improve herself and please other people—so that she can grasp the loving acceptance she craves.

We build our children when we validate them as individuals. With our words, actions, and facial expressions, we should give our children the message that we are happy with them. That we see the beautiful "gardens" growing in their hearts, and value the talents and personal gifts that God has graced to them. And that we are delighted to know them as persons. In the entire human race, each person is uniquely designed to fill a special place in God's kingdom.

As you talk about the future with your children, avoid stereotypes. We tend to talk to little girls about the time when they will marry. Yet it may be God's will for our daughters to serve God as beautiful, competent single women who bless others immeasurably. Sometimes boys are made to feel that they need to enter the ministry to meet their parent's expectations. While being called by God to be ordained is a noble thing, it does not place a higher value on the life of the one who is called. Allow God to order your children's lives, and nurture the process.

Little boys want to be strong. They wonder, "Do I have what it takes to conquer? Can I be strong? Can I meet the test?" On the other hand, little girls want to be beautiful and competent. In their hearts they also ask questions. "Am I lovely? Do I have what it takes to be beautiful? Am I worth having? Do you want me?"

All girls are lovely, and all boys have the potential to become strong men. Our children should know that we truly value them and that we are delighted with them. Both boys and girls look to their fathers for this affirmation. Girls also learn the value of true womanhood as they observe their mothers and grandmothers.

I once came upon a charming little story in my chiropractor's office.

"Mommy," a little girl asked. "What is your favorite bug?"

"Mmmm," the mother answered, grasping for a little time. "I guess I like lightning bugs."

The little girl jumped up and down, clapping her hands. "I'm so glad you said that, Mommy," she answered. "I like lightning bugs too, because I think people should like each other for the light they shine."

Every child should be the star of his mother's heart. A mother was once cutting apples. Instead of halving an apple in the traditional way, she cut the apple in half, leaving the stem on one side and the blossom end on the other.

"See what I have here, children?" she asked, as she showed them the star design. "This is a star. That is like each one of you are in the middle of my heart. I have a star there for each of you. That's how much you mean to me!"

Children develop well emotionally when we respect them as individuals at the same time we are in authority. Our children first belong to God. We are given the stewardship of our children and must carefully and lovingly shape our children to become like their Father in heaven. We will answer to God for our faithfulness or lack of it.

It is good to let children make some of their own choices as they explore who they are as people and as they consider the power they have to impact the world they are in. When you are laying out clothing for the day, you might ask your daughter if she wants to wear her blue dress or her yellow one. At snack time, you might ask your son if he would like an egg or a piece of sausage. Giving the child an opportunity to make some of the choices that belong with his level of maturity will increase his sense of worth and personal volition.

Use this tool when you have an insecure child who makes it his goal to control other people. We all want to control something. Having the option to have some control in his own right may alleviate the strong desire the child feels to control others.

※ ※ ※

We can teach our children some very simple things to aid them in being emotionally secure. A disobedient child is very insecure because he is out of harmony with the authorities in his life. We bless our children tremendously when we teach them to obey. Notice the following basic commands.

- "Come" and "Go" should be the first commands a child learns as he makes choices to submit his will. Does your child come to you when you call him?

- "Give it to me." Does your child willingly hand over the item for which you are asking?

- "Stop." When a child learns to respond to this command, he is not only learning obedience. He is also learning a skill that could save his life.

- "Look at me." Children are much more likely to understand what you say if you first insist that they make eye contact with you.

- Expect a response as soon as possible. Teach them that obedience must be done without delay.

- Teach the child to answer to his own name. If the child is nonverbal, he can be taught to make a noise.

※ ※ ※

I had a family with two children come into my office. The two-year-old daughter was an angelic little girl with golden curls and a sanguine personality, while the five-year-old son was struggling. My heart shuddered when I heard the father comparing the two children, as he often did.

"Why can't you sit still like your little sister can, Todd? Shame on you!" or "Can't you even remember to say, 'Thank you.?' Alisha can." When he spoke to his daughter, he smiled and spoke gently, "Come here, Princess! May I hold you?"

Needless to say, Todd continued to struggle. One day, after I had been working with the family for several months, the father returned to my office after the others were in the car.

"We're missing it somewhere, Joan," he said. "What can I do to help Todd?"

Tears filled my eyes as I answered, "This may sound hard to you. I hope I won't offend you. But I notice that you compliment and praise your little girl, and that you criticize and have hard words for your son. Have you considered what might happen if you call your son your hero, smile into his eyes, and compliment him on his strengths? The boy doesn't know that you love him for who he is."

For a moment the father was speechless. Then tears began to brim from his own eyes.

"I see what you're saying," he replied humbly. "I don't know why I didn't see that before. Thank you, Joan."

Some time later, Todd and his father came into my office again. Todd's eyes were shining, and he walked just like his father.

"Joan," Todd's father spoke with a quaver in his voice, "thank you so much for the way you have helped our family. The formula has worked."

I smiled back. No words were necessary, and as I watched Todd move with happy confidence, there was a lump in my throat that would not have allowed words to come anyway.

chapter four

Further Targeting the Emotional Aspects of the Challenged Child

Following are true stories of real children, with names and details changed for their protection.

Meet Gerald.

I am in grade five and am eleven years old. I don't like to do math—especially not in class, because my classmates snicker and laugh when I simply cannot remember what eight times six is. Nothing about math really makes sense to me—and I've tried to learn as hard as I know how. It makes me feel awful in the bottom of my stomach when the other children laugh at me like that.

When I am working on my lessons, the other children are so wiggly and noisy. I can hardly keep from turning to the side to look at them since I can see them as well as I can see my book. When the day is over, I often have four or five books to take along home. They feel so heavy!

On the way home in the school van, the other children laugh at me and call me Turtle because I am so slow. I curl up in the corner of the van seat behind a book and pretend I'm not there. I don't want the mean children to see the tears that are squeezing out of my eyes. They would laugh again and say I'm a baby. My stomach hurts, and I wish I wouldn't have to go to school anymore.

I'm afraid Dad will spank me. He says I could get more done if I would just try harder. And on top of that, I won't have any time to play with the little kittens tonight—and they're growing so fast. By the time I do my chores, eat supper, and finish my homework, Mom and I will be the only ones up, and I will be so tired that I will hardly be able to hold my eyes open. I wish I wouldn't have to live anymore!

Then there is Anthony.

I am still doing stupid first-grade work—even though I am ten years old. The teacher thinks I am stupid. I know she does. She tells me I need to look at the book and try harder to sound out the words. But how can I do that when I see two of each word, and they slide all over the place? I can hardly decide what the words are. So usually I just guess.

How can Margaret and John, my younger siblings, love to read? It's such hard work, it always gives me a headache. And then I feel like I'm going to throw up. I guess I'm just plain dumb!

Math is really hard for me too. I just can't count the objects right. My teacher asks me how many there are, and I say, "Two." And she says there is only one. She must see a different way than I do, I guess.

I am so dense, I probably won't amount to much. The other day I heard someone talking about a person who is retarded, and he was pointing at me. I wish I could amount to something and hear my teacher, or my mother, telling me what a good job I did. I wish I could matter to somebody and make them happy.

Here is Sarah.

I am eight years old and have cerebral palsy. I have never been able to walk. I can say only a few words, but my mind is bright, and I know exactly what I would like to tell people. I hate when they stare at me like I'm two years old. I wish they would know who I am, and that I could tell someone the poems I make up in my head.

People don't all act unkind. Sometimes people stare at me with such pitying looks—and I figure they mean to be kind. But pity isn't what I want either. It makes me feel so lonely inside—like they think I'm not worth what they are, and they're trying to be nice anyway. I just want people to be my friends, and talk to me like they would to anybody else. And they don't have to talk loudly to me either, because I have good hearing.

There really isn't much that I can do. I can't even scratch my own nose when it's itchy. But I love to listen to people tell stories, and watch them do fun things. Then I can imagine I'm doing it myself.

I hope my family won't forget to take me along when they go to the next room tonight. And I hope my brothers won't jostle my wheelchair too roughly, because I can't catch myself if they spill me out of my wheelchair. I don't know what I would do without my mother. She is the nicest thing about my life, and the only time I feel safe is when I'm with her. When I lie in bed at night, I worry that she will die.

✻ ✻ ✻

Everyone experiences emotions and longs to feel secure, whether he is an adult or a child. We have talked about some of those issues in the previous chapter. Yet challenged children deal with all of these factors, plus a few more.

My heart goes out to the slow learner who is never quite understood. Most people think he should try harder, care more, not be so lazy, or just stick with his work. In all probability, the slow learner has put more time and effort into working with the day's lesson than anyone else in the class. Perhaps he spent more time doing the work than his teacher did in preparing to teach the lesson.

I firmly believe that no child should be required to work from sunup to sundown without breaks and recesses. Yet that is what sometimes happens to our challenged children who are in school. It is very important for these children to have even more time for recreation than the average student. They should have frequent opportunities to refresh their brains—because everything they do takes more effort. If corporal punishment doesn't work, try another route. There are many causes that trigger problems for our children who try so hard, problems that have nothing to do with perverseness.

The challenged student should participate in every recess the class is given. Keeping him in to finish his work is undercutting what he will be able to do for the rest of the day. A mind that is already weary is being deprived of the refreshment it should have to do its best in the next class.

There are also children who function well in school, but only because they drive their resources to the point of exhaustion. These individuals may collapse at some point in life, simply because they have drained their brain energy to the point where the brain finally gives up.

The child who feels genuinely loved and accepted is equipped to do his best. If parents and teachers love their children, but fail to convey the gift of loving acceptance to them, there will be an inner lack in the emotional bases of our children. And they will not be able to perform to their full potential.

Do you know what really makes your child feel loved? How can you make him aware that he is the star of your heart? That you believe in him, and that together you two will make the journey safely—with whatever he is able to do?

I think of 1 John 3:18, where we read, *"My little children, let us not love in word, neither in tongue; but in deed and in truth."* Children read our actions better than our words.

God asked Moses a question we should ask ourselves: *"Who hath made man's mouth? or who maketh the dumb, or deaf, or the seeing, or the blind? have not I the Lord?"* (Exodus 4:11). By this we know that God values all of us equally, and that He has a purpose for the unique situations He brings or allows to enter our lives. Our value to God is not based on our performance, but on the persons we are. Why then are we so naive as to believe that those who have the greatest intelligence, who can run the fastest, or who have the most charming personalities are worth the most?

Understanding this will help us to be at rest in accepting our children as they are—with more resources to meet the high demands of parenting a challenged child. Love your children. Live life with them, and laugh with them. These are the things that make the heart grow, and produce emotionally stable children who are better able to accept themselves as they are—however they may be.

✹ ✹ ✹

For a child to learn well, he must be at the emotional maturity level of the age level that proposed skills or curriculum are based upon. A growing child's ability to learn is based on several other factors as well. But the most important one is his level of emotional maturity.

A child who is starved for love and acceptance will have little motivation for meeting the challenges of school. Since emotional stability and security establishes such an important base in the child's ability to learn, we want to be sure that we prime his learning pump by relating to him in a wholesome way.

How can schoolteachers help challenged children know that they are seen as valid individuals, and that they are appreciated?

Sister Rhoda has a busy, happy special-ed classroom. She puts notes into her students' desks from time to time. If the student is illiterate, she reads the note for him when he brings it to her. He has no trouble enjoying the glossy sticker she attaches.

She chose a tractor sticker and wrote the words "Great work!" on a note for Galen, when he scored 75 percent on a science test. Alice, who has dyslexia, finally reached a breaking-through point where she is able to read more smoothly. She is one happy girl. She and her teacher celebrated when Sister Rhoda put a tiny doll into her desk with a message, "Wonderful!" Timothy's art pictures still leave much to the imagination. But his people are becoming more complete. They usually have necks and legs now—and sometimes eyes. On Timothy's note, Sister Rhoda wrote, "Great job, Timothy! Keep on trying!"

She also chooses special jobs for the students who really have no time to do extra things during the day. Fredrick, one of those hard workers, was delighted to be the one who was assigned to carry the loaf of bread for a senior citizen the class sang for. Sister Rhoda rarely puts a class chart on the wall of her classroom. Instead, students have charts in their workbooks. Her goal is to have the students compete with themselves. If they do better than they did the day before, they get a star.

Some of Sister Rhoda's students rush to their desks when they first come to school, to see if they have a note. If they do, they scurry up to Sister Rhoda, with shining eyes—and they rejoice together. The patrons say that no one else has been able to help their children like their beloved Sister Rhoda does. They attribute that success to the way their children are being loved, valued, and encouraged.

❧ ❧ ❧

Anxiety eats away at the potential of our children. How can you concentrate when you are worrying about something else? And how can you have energy and motivation when your resources are being depleted by the scourge of living in a fight-or-flight mode? Anything that we can do to put our children at rest will facilitate more learning abilities.

It helps our children to be at rest if we take time to slowly explain plans and procedures to them. If we tell them about changes ahead of time, and let them know what to expect, they are able to respond with more calmness. This is very important for nonverbal children.

It also helps a challenged child to feel affirmed if he is given some specific opportunities to make choices for himself. Does he want a red or a blue notebook? What would he like to play for recess? What does he want for his mid-morning snack—a hard-boiled egg, or peanut butter on a cracker?

Mary had a grave problem. She desperately wanted braces on her teeth, just like her friend wore. But Dad said, "No." And her siblings began to snicker when she begged for braces. Finally her mother took her aside.

"Mary," she said, "Do you know why Tracy has braces on her teeth?" When Mary shrugged her shoulders, her mother explained issues very simply. "Tracy's teeth were growing in wrong directions, Mary. So the dentist put each tooth in a pen to pull it the right direction. And sometimes that hurts Tracy. There are some things Tracy can't even eat now.

"But look what I have to show you, Mary," her mother smiled brightly, holding out a hand mirror in front of Mary's face. "Do you see your teeth? They are beautiful, straight teeth that don't need to be straightened. And that is very special! Your teeth are lovely."

Taking the time to explain things—in very simple terms—is important for challenged children. Since her mother explained things to her, Mary is very contented with her lovely teeth. She no longer feels the desire to have braces to make her special. She understands that her own gift of lovely teeth is enough.

Wise parents learn to listen well to their children, and to look at their children while they are speaking to them.

Angela walked into the kitchen while her mother was mixing up cookies. Her mother did not pause, but kept on working as she listened to the child talk. Finally Angela tugged on her mother's skirt. "Mama," she said, "I like it best when you listen with your eyes."

Treasure the gifts your children bring to you. Show your children that you value them by the way you showcase the gifts. Tommy's wilted dandelion is a lovely reminder of his thoughts of love for his mother, perched in a small vase on the kitchen window sill. The pinkish stone that Audrey found in the driveway has a special place on the top of her father's rolltop desk. She climbs up on a chair to look at it every day. Sometimes her father takes it off the shelf and they take it to the window, turning it this way and that, to make the gem parts of the stone sparkle. And then he squeezes her and calls her "Daddy's girl."

Watch homework loads. If your child is continually bogged down with homework, talk to your school board or teacher. A struggling child's work should be cut to the level where he has free time in the evening. Otherwise he does not have the opportunity to develop other parts of his life and to refresh his mind. It is also a good idea to coach him as he does his work. If he is not doing his math correctly, stop him and teach him the right way to do the problem—before the whole lesson is done wrong. Each time the problem is done incorrectly makes it harder to learn the correct way, because the wrong way has been clinched often.

As we have mentioned previously, do not take away a child's recess to punish him. Recesses bring refreshment to tired minds, bringing more oxygen to the brain, and allowing a break in the stresses of academic learning. We all do better when we have those kinds of breaks. For the challenged student, this is particularly true. They also need the interaction on the playground with their fellow students for social development.

One very simple way to lighten a child's workload is to photocopy math problems he would otherwise need to copy himself. If reading problems are difficult, read the problem out loud twice for the child. And if getting the child's answers on paper is problematic, assign someone to listen to his answers and write them for him. For some children, this kind of assistance makes the difference between coping and being overwhelmed. For a dyslexic child, this gift is priceless. For my dyslexic students, I made it a point to plan for time to read test questions to them, and then write the answers they verbally gave me. This worked well when the test was not about how well they could read or write, but only how well they knew the material.

Proper discipline administered with love can spur learning. However, too much spanking is not the answer to helping learning-disabled children. If corporal punishment is to help, you will usually see a difference with one or two punishments for the same offense. If you punish for the same problem time and again, consider that something is obviously wrong—and look for another way to address it.

❋ ❋ ❋

Is your child highly sensitive? Approximately one in five children is born with a highly sensitive nature. These children come across as shy, fearful, and slow to warm up to people in a new situation. Having a sensitive nature is a gift from God. However, if it is not directed carefully, it can produce problems in the life of the child. He may long for friendships but struggle to develop them.

Is someone bullying or abusing your child? Unfortunately, these things can and do happen. Make sure your child will tell you if someone touches him in ways that make him feel uncomfortable. Every four-year-old should be told that there are okay places for other people to touch them, and places that are not okay. We should teach them that the trunks of our bodies and our thigh areas are private places. Our entire bodies are a part of our personal space. So discretion needs to be used in how much we allow other people to touch our arms and shoulders as well.

Sometimes bullies will victimize smaller or weaker children verbally with accusations that they are dumb, stupid, or crazy. They may do their nasty work in a private place and then threaten to beat up the child if he tells on them. This is very damaging to a child, and it should be handled immediately by parents and teachers. Know where your children are, whom they are with and what they are doing.

Inside every child is a tender heart that suffers bumps and bruises from the hurts of life. Ask any adult what hurt him as a child, and waves of stories flow. We remember the harsh responses of parents, the unjust reprimands of a teacher, or a critical observation from a family member. We remember standing on the sidelines, being teased about our weight, or being left out of a birthday party. When faced with the pain of our children, those memories of our own pain can return to the surface, clouding our judgment and limiting our effectiveness to help.

When your child indicates that he fears a caregiver in his life, look seriously at the situation. A child is very vulnerable to people who are given authority over him. Protect him with a sensible, open mind.

Love your spirited child for the person he is. Let him make you laugh. Encourage him to share how he sees, hears, and experiences life. Allow him to enrich your life by entering it with his own.

Soothing Activities for Children

- A soak in the tub.

- Washing dishes or scrubbing potatoes.

- Using play dough or silly putty. Keep a small container in your purse for the child to play with in the car. Or keep little fidgets in your purse for times such as waiting in the doctor's office.

- Chewing gum.

- Using shaving cream to finger paint.

- Getting back rubs or numbers written on their back with your finger.

- Being read to, or reading for themselves.

- Getting "time out" when you see that a crisis is developing. Break the cycle with a quiet space.

- Being caught by your eye. Instead of calling to him, go over to your child and look him in the eye. If necessary, hold the child's chin in your hand and tell him to look at you.

- Being told when a change is about to take place.

- Being coached through disappointments. Disappointments are transitions that are difficult for challenged children to handle. Teach the child how to respond to situations by asking what they would do if (1) they are served fruit salad instead of cake; (2) someone in the family would get sick, and they cannot visit Uncle Abners'. How would the child feel? What would the child do to handle the situation? This teaches the child to develop coping strategies.

- Taking frequent breaks.

- Feeling a gentle hand on his shoulder.

- Being complimented for noble accomplishments.

- Using a wiggle seat. These are known as tactile cushions and can be found at teacher's stores.

- Using a fidget toy.

❋ ❋ ❋

Symptoms in a child that should raise questions in a teacher's mind:

- Is too quiet in class—The child has nothing to say, and cannot offer an answer when you call on him.

- Has poor self-image; feels worthless and like he is no good.

- Does not participate in lunch time discussions; has little interaction with others.

- Does not join in games at recess; stands to the side by himself.

- Does not get the drift of conversations.

- Cannot catch a joke or a "play" on words.

- Is easily frustrated; dissolves into tears or goes to hide.

- Acts out.

- Pushes or trips others quietly and on the sly.

- Cannot handle change; becomes even quieter.

Children are precious gifts on loan from God. What a blessing it is to find ways to help them thrive and bloom!

chapter five

Discipline and the Challenged Child

Part I—General Thoughts Regarding Discipline

We have a problem in the world today. Children are growing up without having been guided and trained to become whole, happy adults who are prepared to sacrifice for the kingdom of God. Without anchors, many of them become selfish adults who live for themselves—largely because their parents have not taught and trained them in a Biblical pattern.

The value of the individual has been distorted into the belief that each individual is special in his own right, and should follow his "inner light." Dr. Spock taught a generation that a child's wants are his legitimate needs, and American history has told the story his theory produces.

Quality time—what is that? Are we satisfied with some hurried conversation in the evening, after everyone's best resources have been spent in other ways during the day? Day care centers and broken homes are producing children whose hearts are in shreds.

And then there is the other extreme. So much is written now about listening, and spending time with children, that some well-meaning parents are putting their children in charge, and becoming their personal entertainers. The fallout of this problem is equally damaging.

One or two generations ago, young people grew up understanding a disciplined life, and carried with them the framework to train their own children. Today young people are moving into home responsibilities without really knowing how to train and nurture the precious children God loans to them.

In a world that confuses issues because people do not want to accept responsibility for their personal actions, we need strong, wise, caring parents who first know God and take the cross seriously. Only then will they be ready and equipped to know the balances of law and grace, and how to discipline and train their children in love.

God is calling for a generation of parents who will go back to the source that never changes—God and the Bible. When we repent and return to God's ways, He will be there to bring harmony into our lives and homes.

God commands parents to be in authority. Child training, consistently and wisely administered, carries with it a tremendous reward of blessing—for time and for eternity. When God created His plan for mankind, he instituted families as the basic components of human society. Each parent becomes a steward of the trust God has given to him or her. A proper understanding of and use of this authority brings harmony into our lives. For God has commanded parents to be in authority over their children.

We will answer directly to God for our use or abuse of this authority. Therefore we must understand the principles of the authority God has given us, so we can fulfill our stewardship. As we fulfill our stewardship, our word will become law to our children, and our children are responsible to do what we instruct them to do. This in turn makes us responsible for the actions of our children.

A child does have needs. A child cries when he is hungry, when he has stubbed his toe, and so on. However, when a child cries because his will has been crossed, that is not a need—but his sinful nature asserting itself in rebellion.

Screaming is a control tactic that seeks to terrorize others. Never give the child anything he screams for—or he will learn to control you with his screaming.

We build a base for emotional security when we teach a child to control his emotions by teaching him which responses are acceptable and which are not. We accomplish this by teaching the child to think rightly.

Love does what is best for its beloved. Love motivates parents to read to and cuddle their children. It also requires that they discipline their children for wrongdoing, correcting them. To correct means to redirect into the right way.

Maintaining Parental Authority

- Be in charge. Accept the role of authority God has given to you. Direct the child with clear commands. Then the child will be at rest and will blossom.

- Punish the child when he disobeys you the first time.

- Use a firm, kind manner and tone of voice that indicates

command. Limit your words. Calmly and clearly say what you mean once. Do not be an apologetic parent.

· Refuse to let your child order you, or be in charge.

· Do not relate to the child with a continual string of questions. Neither should you ask him how he feels about your directives.

· Teach accountability. The child must learn that he is to obey regardless of what anyone else says or does. If he is punished when someone else is not, the issue at stake is that he did wrong.

· The child must be under authority as long as he is in the parental home. If he lives there after he is an adult, he is still responsible to respect the values of the home.

Spending Time Together Profitably
· Set the pace. Do not feel selfish if you do what you decide to do instead of what the child wants.

· Within reason, make the child a participant revolving around someone else's will, rather than his own.

· Be issue—and activity—oriented, rather than focusing on feelings.

· Affirm the child with honest praise. But do not do so at the expense of taking away his satisfaction in simply knowing that he has done the right thing. This mentality goes back to establishing the fear of God in your child's experience.

The central idea of child training is not complex. Simply tell the child what he is expected to do, and consistently punish him when he disobeys. Then the child cannot control the atmosphere, he becomes happy and at rest, and the home blossoms.

Beginning By Exercising Control

We begin child training by controlling our children, and then move into teaching and training them, developing the framework that will help them to become disciplined, humble men and women of God.

God has put tools and gifts within our reach that help us teach our children to follow Him. His Word gives us the basic principles that every parent needs to train his child. If we truly love our children, we will obey these commands—so that both we and they can experience the blessings God longs to give to His children.

Training follows a logical sequence. Before we can instruct and train our children, we must exercise control in teaching them to obey. This learned obedience teaches them to respect us. After they respect us, they are prepared to receive our instruction. Without respect, children will not receive instruction. We see the fruit of parental honor when our children respect us enough to wisely accept our advice and instructions.

True love for God can come only after we have learned to respect Him. This is also true in parenthood. Before a child can really love his parents, he must first develop a base of respect.

Effective child training, like God's directives for marriage, brings blessing even to those who do not know God. However, only those who know God's Word and are filled with His Spirit will be able to *"bring them up in the nurture and admonition of the Lord"* (Ephesians 6:4). The Greek word bring is a very tender word which means to cherish or train, while nurture carries the thought of disciplinary correction. Admonition speaks of warning and rebuke.

Sponges can be shaped. Our children become what they are because we have trained them to be that way. We are responsible. What a blessing to train and shape a child for God!

63

Every generation is a new generation who has not yet experienced the fullness of God's goodness. Each day brings new opportunities to rise and build. May we be faithful in our generation. Throughout time, there must be a line of godly men and women who are actively teaching and training the next generation.

Parents symbolize God's authority to their children. If you require that your child obeys you, he will respect you. Upon that foundation, he will also learn to respect other authorities in his life, and ultimately God Himself.

Part II —Dealing with Neurologically Damaged Children

When we deal with neurologically damaged or abused children, we sometimes find that patterns that work with a child who has had a secure background do not work the same way. If you have spanked your child three or four times in one week for a misdeed without getting through, something is not connecting. A proper response to punishment depends on good neurological function and the ability to comprehend what is being taught. If the child is not able to respond appropriately, continual punishment will be damaging.

We must find ways that keep the parent in charge, and provide for the training and nurture of the child in ways that will bless—rather than damage him. Every parent who has a challenged child needs to ask God for wisdom and use sound judgment. There will be exceptions to every rule. Often the most important thing to remember is simply to be cheerfully and confidently in charge. And the child will naturally seek to follow you.

Our expectations will be different for a challenged child than they will be for his sibling who has normal, healthy neurological development. Learn to know your child so that you can establish a reasonable base from which to work.

Look for reasons that explain why the child may be acting out. If you can, take care of that problem. (For example, see Chapter Two, where protein needs are discussed.) If your baby is unreasonably fussy, make sure the diaper pin is not poking him. Provide a calm, secure environment so the child can absorb strength.

When parents are facing out-of-hand temper tantrums in a damaged child, one approach is to pick the child up and hold him firmly until he calms down. If the child is not able to process discipline, simply falling apart when he is disciplined, sometimes using distraction works best.

There are also times when taking away a privilege serves as useful discipline. Jeffrey loved taking care of his dog. When the dog saw him coming to fill his food dish, he was delighted to see Jeffrey. When Jeffrey became very careless with his food at the table, his mother removed his privilege of feeding the dog. The problem at the table soon cleared up.

Realizing that they would need to withhold privileges as correction, John and Kathy implemented several activities or opportunities that did not involve anything essential to their daughter's necessary daily routines. One of these was the privilege of getting the mail. Now Kathy has the option of withholding one of those as a correctional tool.

Sometimes a small disciplinary measure will be all it takes to get your child's attention. Depending on the child, you may also want to send him to his room to think about what he did after a misdemeanor. You can have the child sit quietly, and leave him there to think about what he has done. Increase the time as the child can handle it, or according to the degree of disobedience.

Sometimes "time in" is more effective. Direct the child to sit on a small rug right beside you, wherever you are. While the child is being disciplined, he is not removed from you, and can still sense your support and acceptance in a present, active way. And you can talk to him. Depending on the situation, you may want to give the child something to do while he sits there, such as play with a little truck, or look at a book. Do not use the specified rug for anything else. This method is helpful when a child carries a fear of abandonment.

Do not make more rules than you will be able to enforce for your child. Then carry out correction when he disobeys. That way he will develop a sense of respect for your authority. And your words will mean something.

Use clear, literal language as you speak to your child. Otherwise he may fail to grasp what you are saying, not understanding your thought or directive. Children lack the common sense they may develop later in life. So avoid hyperboles and idioms. Otherwise, they may miss the point you are trying to make.

When a child has trouble processing information, try this approach. After you have given him direction and he fails to comprehend what you expect him to do, Say, "Stop, and think about that." When the problem is auditory delay, where the brain needs longer to process the signals from the ear, this will help immensely.

It is good to stop and ponder how the child actually feels. Often the child feels very much alone and unloved, as if nobody understands him. A lot of these children wonder whether their parents really do love them, since they view themselves as being abnormal and ugly. They feel frustrated at themselves for being so dumb!

It is necessary to keep yourself strongly in check as you deal with your child, if you feel emotionally triggered. Even as you discipline your child, surround your child with a sense of calm strength upon which he can lean. Let him know that you love him deeply, but that you are disappointed with his behavior. And that you will insist that he learns to cooperate with you. Children need these kinds of boundaries if they are to be secure.

Since our challenged children are generally very negative in their outlook, we need to be positive in the way we respond, and in the way we present life to them. If we act defeated, or react to them by fighting with them, everyone will be in trouble. The key thought is to be calmly in charge. If you feel emotionally overwhelmed when a misdemeanor occurs, ask your spouse to take care of the situation for you. That is one of the reasons God gave a child two parents.

※ ※ ※

It is important to understand how difficult transition is for children who struggle neurologically. If you need to handle something that is difficult with the child, do it at a time when the child is not facing other stresses. Putting toys away, getting a bath, and going to bed as the day winds down becomes the worst time of day for some children. The child is now expected to move from an enjoyable activity (playing with his toys) to something that may seem strange or even frightening to him.

Rachel looks at Timothy who is playing quietly (for a change) with his toys on the living room floor. It is almost bedtime, and she grimaces as she remembers two-year-old Timothy's tantrums last evening, when it was time to get ready for bed and nothing would make him happy. Perhaps if she helps him be more prepared for the change, things will go better.

"That's a beautiful block tower you're making, Timothy," Rachel says in a calm, cheerful tone. "I like it. Do you see my buzzer?"

Timothy looks up at the chicken-shaped timer Rachel holds in her hand, and nods. Then he turns absently back to his blocks.

"Look, Timothy," Rachel says, as she kneels beside him to show him the timer. "You like my buzzer, don't you? Look at what I'm going to do. We're going to set this timer for five minutes, and when it rings, the chicken will be telling you, 'Timothy, it's almost time for a story. Put your toys away." Then I want you to put the toys away."

"Um." Timothy nods and smiles as he looks at Rachel's face. "Chick buzz."

When the timer rings, Rachel comes into the living room with Timothy's pajamas and a storybook. "Look what I have, Timothy," she smiles. "Your froggie pajamas! And we're going to read a story when you're all cozy and ready for bed." She kneels beside him. "Here, Timothy. Put your blocks back into this bucket."

"Um," he says again. He is not smiling. But neither is Timothy distressed.

"Good job, Timothy!" Rachel says as she sets the filled bucket in the corner. "And now it's pajama time. Come here."

Timothy looks at the bucket of blocks. Then his eyes turn toward his mother.

"Um," he says. "Me come."

"That's a good boy," says Rachel as she lifts him onto her lap and kisses him. "Did you have fun playing with the blocks?"

"Um," Timothy answers.

"And now it's time for something else. We'll put your pajamas on, and then I'll read to you about the lost milk jar. You like that story!"

"Tory," Timothy smiles and nods. "Um."

Things go well until it is time to put Timothy into his youth bed. Timothy begins to whimper and cry.

"Do you feel sad about going to bed?" asks Rachel. "Tomorrow will be another day, and then we'll get your blocks out again."

"Ing," begs Timothy.

"Sure we'll sing a song," says Rachel. "I'll sing to you about the stars in the sky. God is watching us. He loves us very much."

"Um," Timothy says, and sighs sleepily.

Ten minutes later, Rachel tiptoes out of the bedroom, with a sigh of relief. No temper tantrums tonight! "Thank you, Lord," she breathes a prayer heavenward.

If you are calm and peaceful, your own anxieties will not add fuel to your child's coping distress. As a parent uses an upbeat, cheerful attitude and creates a buoyant, in-charge home atmosphere, it will go a long way in avoiding problems before they have a chance to begin.

Notice that Rachel set the pace for Timothy's transition. Damaged children need routine. They need someone who sets the pace and is in charge. They feel very much at sea with a passive parent.

Rachel was also understanding, and provided for Timothy's care. She created an ideal situation for trust to develop and be maintained. Damaged children need an endless amount of loving care and reassurance.

In dealing with situations where discipline is used, make sure that you apply the discipline while the child still remembers what his offense has been. Otherwise it will only frustrate both of you.

Sometimes we need to use unusual methods to unlock a problem situation with our challenged children. One of my special-ed students and I experienced a time like that. Lunch time had became a nightmare for both Tracy and me when she was going through an extended period when she simply did not want to eat. I was in tears when I went to bed at night. How could Tracy live and function well if she would not eat? A visit from the principal became a normal part of our lunch time, as I fought to get some nutrition into the eight-year-old. We tried everything—punishments, distractions, promised rewards, ignoring the problem, and working on it intensely.

Finally my principal called me aside. "Joan," he said, "Something isn't working here. We have to try something different. Tomorrow give Tracy the choice of whether or not she wants to eat."

"You mean let her go without eating anything?" I asked incredulously. "I'm sure she won't want to eat."

"Yes," he replied evenly. "She won't starve right away. She still has a few extra pounds." I watched him depart with questions in my eyes. My principal was a wise man. But would this work?

Tracy tensed for the fight as I approached her seat at noontime the next day. "We're going to do something different today, Tracy," I said, smiling at her. "We're going to let you choose whether or not you want to eat."

First she looked shocked. "Don't!" she declared firmly.

"All right," I said, "You can take your lunch box back to the shelf."

That was Monday. Tuesday, Wednesday, Thursday and Friday were the same. But as I continued to give Tracy the choices, I began to see a little bit of softness in Tracy's face by the end of the week.

The next Monday we started out a little differently. "Now, Tracy," I said, with a confident smile, "today I'm going to help you eat three bites of your sandwich. And then you can choose if you want more. But you can't say 'Don't' until you have eaten three bites of each thing."

She began eating her sandwich hesitantly, trying to figure me out. We followed the same pattern with her fruit and her celery. She ate the three bites. But after the three bites were eaten, she closed her mouth and then declared, "Don't." But she was cooperating according to plan, and she was eating food.

Things continued in that fashion for two more weeks. Then the required serving became four bites. And when Tracy said "Don't" after the four bites, we quit. This was not the best way to eat lunch. But at least it was one way.

Two months later, I simply stayed at my desk during the entire lunch period. Out of the corner of my eye, I watched Tracy watching me as she calculated her possibilities. But then the smell of her ham sandwich overcame her, and she took a bite. Before long it was gone. Next she opened her fruit, took one bite and put the rest in her lunch box. And we merged back into normal lunch times again.

So keep trying. Sometimes the power of choice may be the tool that will unlock the door. If one method doesn't work, try another. When our children do the best they can do, they are doing well. The same principle is true for parents, teachers and principals.

Search for ways to show respect to your children so they are affirmed as valid persons. Challenged children, who cannot fit into society well, feel shame and a sense of worthlessness. Build them up as individuals with your own acceptance. And when they do things well, make sure to tell them that you noticed.

God deals with us wisely, gently, firmly, and with loving kindness. Sometimes He deals with us in unexpected ways. Yet He never changes who He is, and He works for our best. God is delighted to be with us, and sees and treasures the centers of our beings.

May God help us to do the same with our damaged treasures.

chapter six

The General Pattern of Child Development

The contents of this chapter could fill an entire set of books. What we offer here are some guiding principles rather than any kind of inclusive review.

As I work with the children I love and with their parents, I ask some very important questions that sketch a picture for me. At what age did the parent begin to suspect a problem? When did the child crawl? And when did he sit alone? When did he begin walking? Was it always hard for the child to make eye contact?

As I devise programs, I follow a certain sequence. As we begin the program, we take the child back to the months he was in utero, and then through the first year's development in the order development should have happened, to reprogram the brain to function properly. After that I move to development that should take place in the second year and beyond, continuing to fill in the missing gaps for the child. This is because God's system of normal childhood development first develops the lower part of the brain and then moves on to the higher levels. As I work with children, I follow the same pattern. Otherwise, it can be like trying to put a roof on a house before the foundation is in place. And the brain struggles.

When the child is in his mother's womb, and as he develops as a baby, a definite progression of reflexes emerge, one after the other, to build a healthy central nervous system (CNS). We notice parts of the sequence as our children learn to hold their heads up, sit up, crawl and walk. When a reflex moves into play, we say it is emerging. When it is retired by the emergence of the next reflex, we say it is integrating. These reflexes, like a tower of blocks, need to occur in the proper order, and then become dormant in the lower brain, in a continuing series so that the adult postural control can develop.

The Bible tells us that *"God hath not given us the spirit of fear; but of power, and of love, and of a sound mind."* (II Tim. 1:7) Mothers should be aware of the ways fear in their own lives extends to the way their children develop. This happens while the baby is still in the womb. When fear grips the child, his developing reflexes will not be able to move through healthy neurological development. A child will quickly sense fear in his mother. Children also learn from the way their parents live. Children who have been affected by their mother's fears are likely to have emotional, academic and physical challenges because their brains and nervous systems have been compromised.

When trauma occurs in the child's life, whether it is emotional or physical, the reflex sequence is often disturbed. If this is not corrected, the child develops problems in his CNS. He may have trouble with mental processing, vision, and hearing. He may also have severe challenges with vestibular and balance issues—his ability to pay attention, comprehend, and cope with stress. Since the various functions of the brain and the CNS are so involved with one another, we generally find groups of problems in children, rather than one isolated problem.

We work with various aspects of the brain in babies, children and adults. The following list shows some of the things we look for as we evaluate our clients.

Brain Balance

Are the two sides of the brain working together in a healthy balance? Or is one too active and doing most of the work? When this happens, the sides cannot work well together. If not corrected, the individual has trouble functioning normally, and struggles very hard to perform. The individual is then at risk to suffer a nervous breakdown when stresses become overwhelming.

Without a healthy balance between the two hemispheres of the brain, individuals suffer multitudes of problems. Some of these are lack of balance and coordination, poor fine motor skills, difficulty in concentration and comprehension, and poor social skills.

Dominance Issues

Either the right or left side of the brain should become dominant in each individual. A child should freely use both sides of his brain until he is perhaps a year and a half to two and a half years old, so that both sides of his brain have the opportunity to develop. The dominant foot develops after the child is walking well. The dominant hand becomes apparent when the child is about two or three, and the dominant ear when he is about five or six. Eye dominance finally develops when the child is perhaps six or seven. This means that some children are going to school, where hand-eye coordination is very important, before their central nervous systems are ready.

When an individual is right ear dominant, left eye dominant, left leg dominant and right hand dominant—the brain is working in a constant state of confusion and clutter that makes learning and living difficult. Bedwetting is often a telltale sign here.

Before a dominance has been established, the brain doesn't know which hand or foot it should use to do something. So every time the child lifts a spoon to his mouth or kicks a ball, the brain has to ask, "Which hand/foot should I use?" This fatigues the brain and destroys efficiency.

Retained Primitive Reflexes

Primitive reflexes that are active after they should not be bring glitches into our neurological function. By repeating the same motions a baby should have made at the time these primitive reflexes should have been in the process of becoming integrated, we are able to address the brain to integrate them, and move on toward mature postural control.

There are many reflexes in a child's development. One example of retained primitive reflexes is the Fear Paralysis Reflex, which should be active in a fetus from about the fifth to the twelfth week of pregnancy. What should have served to protect the baby for a period of time during the pregnancy remains, and locks children into a pattern of fear where they live in a fight-or-flight mode. The body doesn't know how to relax because it is constantly on guard, and its adrenal, emotional and mental resources are fatigued. This produces very brittle children who cannot transition well, who find it hard to respond well to discipline, and who are not well adjusted in general. They are always running from the "tiger."

After we work with these primitive reflexes in hyperactive children, we see children who are able to sit quietly in a chair. And when we therapists work with RAD children, we see the children unwind emotionally and become better able to trust and live productively.

Some other common retained primitive reflexes include the rooting reflex that at one time helped a baby to nurse, as well as the Babinski and Palmar reflexes. Children with these retained reflexes are the ones whose mouths hang open, and who chew on their shirts and pencils.

If you have an infant who doesn't nurse well, rub his palms and the soles of his feet to enhance the suckle reflex. It is interesting that mothers tend to do these two things without knowing why they are doing them.

❀ ❀ ❀

When we speak of a cross-lateral pattern, we refer to the use of a child's arms and legs, where the right arm and the left leg should be in motion at the same time. Then the child should switch to the left arm and the right leg. Realizing how important it is for a child to crawl with a good cross-lateral pattern, what should a mother do when her child is not inclined to crawl for the four to five months that are needed for the brain to develop during the crawling stage?

Sandra brought her eight-month-old baby to me. I watched the child move about on the floor. Instead of crawling with a good cross-lateral pattern, she scooted awkwardly forward as she pulled with one leg—dragging the other one behind her.

"Why does my baby crawl like this, Joan?" Sandra asked as she lifted troubled eyes to me.

"Your baby should have spent more time on her tummy," I answered.

"I was afraid you would say that," Sandra answered. "What do I do now?"

"First," I said, "put the baby on the floor on her tummy often. Even if she gets up soon, she'll still get some practice. And then I'll give you exercises to develop the part of the brain that got missed."

Remember—the best place for babies to explore the world is on the floor. Even if they can get up on their own, put them down. Like Sandra's baby, they will still get some practice in the process.

Angela brought her fourteen-month-old baby into my office and slumped wearily into a chair.

"What's wrong with my baby, Joan?" she asked. "She doesn't sleep well at night, and is very fussy in the daytime."

I watched the child for a while. Then I asked, "How long did she crawl, Angela?"

"She started crawling at seven and a half months, and started walking two weeks later," Angela answered. "What should I have done?"

"You should have followed her around the house, putting her down on the floor every time she pulled herself up," I answered. "That way more of the necessary brain connections could have been made."

"And what do we do now?" asked Angela.

"Get down on the floor and crawl with her. Model crawling. Babies do what their parents do. Make a game of it and have fun together. Play tag. Between you and your husband, make sure that your baby crawls for thirty minutes a day."

Stephanie looked at the eleven-month-old baby on her lap.

"Which hand should she be using to eat, Joan?"

"Both," I said. "Until your child is about two years old, she needs to use both hands so the brain develops both sides as the hands are used. We don't want a dominance to develop yet. Actually, I prefer seeing children eat with their hands at this age. That way they will probably use both the left and the right sides, and their minds have the opportunity to develop through the sense of touch as the fingers touch the food. They need to feel different textures.

"And if you give her a spoon," I continued, "lay the spoon in front of her on her high chair tray. See which hand she wants to use to pick it up. But we don't want her dominance to develop for about another year, because she needs to be developing both sides of her brain and body right now."

Stacy was a little girl who was out of tune with life. When I first evaluated her, she showed right dominance with her hand and left dominance with her eye and ear. Her feet could never quite decide which one was dominant.

I shared my notes with Stacy's mother at the end of the evaluation. "It looks like we have a leftie who has been taught to use her right hand," I began. "Stacy chooses to use her left ear and left eye, and her foot is undecided. Can you remember anything about which hand she wanted to use when she learned to use a spoon?"

Stacy's mother's mouth dropped open. "I never thought of that, Edith," she said. "Well, yes. She wanted to use her left hand, and we taught her she needed to hold the spoon in her right hand—because I thought that was the right way to eat and write. Does that matter?"

"Yes," I said, "it does. There is no correct hand to use. The brain needs to decide which side will be dominant. And if we force the wrong side, we damage brain development. How would you feel about letting her switch to holding her spoon and pencil in her left hand?"

"If you say so," she said. "Will that help her neurologically?"

"Yes," I answered. "Right now she has mixed dominance, which means her brain is confused about which hemisphere is supposed to take the lead. The brain will be better able to rewire itself if we take that confusion away. We'll watch for bedwetting. If that doesn't happen, we'll know we've done the right thing."

We tried the experiment, and Stacy did well. The next time I saw her, she had more confidence and more light in her eyes.

"We're very happy with the way things are going," her mother said. "We're doing her list of exercises every day, seven days a week."

"Very good!" I exclaimed. "Stacy's brain can reorganize better now that it isn't confused about the dominance issue. And you're doing great with therapy. Did you know that the length of time therapy needs to be done is twice as long if you miss one day a week?"

"Oh, no," she said. "So it matters that much?"

We applaud our faithful mothers who stick with their programs day in and day out. And they are the ones who see the best results—soonest—with their children.

Describing the Neurologically Damaged Child

What is hyperactivity? We say that a child is hyperactive when he is unreasonably active, unable to sit still or stand still. He is not able to focus on any one thing for more than a few seconds.

We expect a two-year-old to be active, and a toddler will find it easier to run than to stand still. There is a reason for this. More balance skill is required for standing still than for running. So when we are at risk neurologically, we run, jump, somersault and skip.

Food allergies can also contribute to this. Tony was definitely in the autistic spectrum. He exhibited lots of strange behavior. One of them was crawling while dragging his head on the floor—or lying on the sofa with his head hanging down.

Tony's pediatrician suggested food allergy testing. We were not surprised when we learned he was highly intolerant to milk. After two weeks off all dairy, Tony was acting nearly normal, and he explained what he had been experiencing. He told us that the continual pressure that made his head feel like it was going to pop was now gone. Feeling that pressure was the reason he had been dragging his head on the floor.

Tony's mother communicated with his teacher that Tony's tolerance for milk products was zero, and she provided a non-dairy snack to be used if the class was treated to a dairy product.

One day Tony came home from school and returned to his pattern of crawling while dragging his head on the floor. He was again nonverbal. Feeling intense concern, his mother called the schoolteacher. Had Tony had anything to eat with milk in it that day?

The teacher pondered possibilities. At first her answer was negative. Then she remembered that they had done an art project, using a slice of White American cheese—and that Tony probably had eaten his.

So Tony's problems had returned. Since Tony was highly allergic to the least bit of milk, his brain had swollen. The pressure in his head had returned, destroying his well-being. We were all delighted when, after two weeks, Tony was back to his new normal again.

Some children cannot concentrate because their pupils are open so wide that they see more than they should. This brings in tremendous amounts of stimuli that they will have reason to respond to. This happens when the two hemispheres of the brain are not working together as a team. These same children may also be supersensitive to what they hear.

Children act the way they feel. Sometimes the hyperactive child becomes a risk to his siblings as he vents the anger and frustration of his own misery on them. Protect your other children if this occurs.

The challenged child can also be difficult to connect with. We find it hard to build relationships when we are frustrated with life. A parent can help this problem by working to build a bond between himself and his child. When the child learns to know his parent as his first companion, he learns to move smoothly into other relationships as well.

Food Allergies or Emotional Issues???

The mother's health will affect the baby she bears. Were you in good health for several years before your child was born? The physical health of the mother (and the father) affect the genes that will be given to their offspring. In some cultures, where children are typically born with strong bodies and minds, both parents are on special diets before the child is conceived, to provide nourishing food for their own bodies—so that the gift can then be passed to their offspring.

We have moved far from the perfect genetics God gave to Adam and Eve, and the genetic base of the average person now has flaws. When our diets are poor, the flaws that are in our genetic bases are able to present—sometimes as neurological problems. When our diets are rich in nourishing, life-giving food, our genes are able to correct some of their negative effects. However, it is important to note that what it has taken four generations of parents who eat well to rebuild, can be lost in one generation—when junk food wears down the body's defenses to illness and degeneration. The brains and constitutions of today's children are being squandered in the name of selfish personal choices.

When a man and a woman marry, it is important that they consider the legacy they will give to the generations that follow them. Individuals who are more closely related than third cousins are contributing to genetic breakdown. Some of the birth defects and genetic weaknesses that follow a closely-related marriage may not be apparent until the third or fourth generation. By that time, it can affect many people. This issue becomes a major problem when a group of people continue to marry without much diversity in genetics, and when couples continue to marry their second cousins.

I remember the white-haired man who told us about his courtship and marriage to his second cousin. His eyes smiled as he related, "We just came to love each other so much that we didn't want to be parted."

However, payday is here now. The second generation of the family line suffered genetic issues relating to sleep and mental processing. Some individuals in the third generation are adults who find it hard to function. And the problem in their descendents is mushrooming. But the defective genes cannot be recalled. And they will continue to be passed to succeeding generations.

It is also important to remember that the genetics that you pass to your child will affect your daughter's children as well. The essence that will become your daughter's eggs are already present when she is born. One generation cannot look lightly at their responsibility for the well-being of their legacy. God will hold us responsible for our choices.

Do you have food allergies? Is your immune system functioning well? Do you have Lyme disease? And what about the amount of rest you are getting? All these will affect the little ones you bear.

You will also be a better parent if you are eating a nourishing diet that helps you present with good attitudes and life skills. A body and mind that are starved for real food will not be able to function well neurologically. And individuals affected by this problem will find it more difficult to function well as parents.

Having a mind that functions well also aids us in our spiritual walk and in following Christ. The reason? God reaches us through our mind and emotions. And when we are not mentally and emotionally well, our spiritual progress is impeded.

The tiny baby you carry in utero knows if you are delighted that he is in your womb—or if you resent his presence. He will be affected by the fear patterns you live by, or by the freedom with which you live. Bonding begins long before the baby is born. The tiny baby who has not been wanted before birth feels abandoned, and will have difficulty bonding. Let your unborn child hear loving voices and gentle words. Sing songs. And maintain a calm spirit that will lay the basis for his emotional security. Someone has suggested that the greatest gift a father can give his unborn child is to shelter and bless his wife, so that her life is as wholesome and stress-free as possible.

If you or your husband have poor neurological organization due to your genetic bases, your child may be born with the same tendency. There are also other reasons for neurological disorders. Deliveries that come too fast, or last too long, take a toll on the baby. C-sections are also hard on our babies. A cord around the neck at birth presents problems for the child, as well as premature births. (See Chapter 15 on Overcoming Specific Obstacles.) Add to this the falls and bumps your child experiences—particularly if he strikes his head. Heads are precious. Beautiful promise can be permanently lost in the split second it takes a child's head to impact a hard surface.

Following is a list of things that you can do to prevent neurological problems in your baby:
- Give the child tummy time from Day One. This can be done in increments that add up throughout the day.

- The best place for a baby is on the floor—not in a walker, jumper, infant seat or swing.

- Lots of head rubbing is an excellent way to organize neurological function.

- Play with the child's fingers and toes.

- If you decide to use vaccines, they do less damage after the baby's immune system is more developed. Under no conditions is it safe to give several at one time. And if this is done, the damage is magnified if they are all given in the same arm or leg.

I remember Tina, a four-year-old child who became damaged after she was given multiple vaccines in one day. She stared around the room with a strange, empty look in her eyes. Tina was constantly on the move, and it was difficult for her to learn. She had almost no bond with her mother. There is little that sickens one's heart more than seeing a child with all the life, innocence and delight gone from his eyes.

And I think of Gary, a challenged seventeen-year-old who struggles to mesh with his peers with a mind than cannot function optimally. He was a promising baby, developing speech before he received a routine baby vaccine. At that point, he lost the words he had been gaining—and after that, everything became hard. So much can be lost with a single shot that ruins the child's neurological system.

- Make sure that you are eating good foods, and nurse your child as long as possible. Nursing does many things, including training the child's immune system how to respond.

- Build up the child's immune system with good food, quality vitamins and etc.

- Don't give your infant pasteurized milk before he is two years old, and no gluten until he is at least one year old.

- A child with neurological issues should be off dairy, gluten and refined sugars.

- Make sure you are supporting the child emotionally. Does he feel loved, wanted and treasured by you? Do you use pet names that build him up and make him feel cherished?

- Present good role models to your children. Men should be strong, active, wise protectors. Women should be competent, gracious individuals who are at peace with themselves—and give that aura to everyone they touch.

Check this list for signs of neurological trouble:
- Does the child take only five-to fifteen-minute naps?

- Is it difficult for your child to hold his head up when he is placed on his tummy?

- Does the child suffer earaches?

- Does he have rashes? They indicate allergies.

- Does your baby often fuss and spit up?

- Does your baby have trouble bonding?

This is a point of special concern for adoptive parents. A large part of bonding occurs before the age of two. Without proper bonding, the child will not have good neurological function. Parents should hold and rock their children freely. Rocking in a rocking chair is brain therapy, and a must for development. (Adoptive parents should rock their sons and daughters even if they are past the age when we usually rock children.) If your baby is adopted, do not let people outside the family hold him for at least the first three months. This is to help him develop his basic bond to his mother.

How can a parent deal with these neurological red flags waving, and work harmoniously with the child?

Consider the following points:

- Seek to understand what the child is seeing and experiencing in his life. How does he feel?

- What is the probable cause of threat in the child's life? Consider what could be overtaxing his coping abilities. Is someone tormenting the child at home or at school? Or when he is at church? Is anyone abusing the child physically or emotionally?

- Create an atmosphere of openness with the child that invites him to share with you. Ask gentle, probing questions about what he and his friends have been doing; what people said to him; and how he felt after a situation occurred. When the child comes to you with a fear or concern, listen to his story without interrupting or accusing him.

- When he has done wrong, deal with him as God does with us— kindly, but firmly. If others are taking advantage of him, step out and intervene. You are his protector.

- If you suspect sexual abuse, act promptly and decisively. Sexual abuse warps the minds and souls of children and grieves the heart of God!

- Learn to truly listen to your child. Be comfortably in charge, and then step out to surround the child with your strength and caring. Look into your child's eyes when he talks to you. Pay attention with your heart and mind.

- Find out what kind of gifting from others makes your child feel loved.

- Some children especially desire the gifting of being appropriately touched—a hug, a hand on the shoulder, a squeeze or holding his hand.

- For others, personal quality time, where they can share deeply in a one-on-one relationship, speaks volumes to their souls. When you look at one of these children, make sure you look into his eyes when you talk to him.

- Others thrive on receiving gifts. This could be a small, green pebble from a friend, a card from a favorite aunt, or the new doll a little girl receives for her birthday. Gifts carry a special message of love to the hearts of these children.

- Words of affirmation are very building to another group of children. They thrive on honest commendation. When you say, "You did a wonderful job, Henry. I appreciate it!" his heart is buoyed up to reach the next conquest in his life.

- Some children are pleased by deeds of service that others gift to them. They are delighted when someone runs an errand for them, hands them a stack of clothes that were lovingly laundered for them, or sweeps their room as an unexpected gift.

※※ ※※ ※※

Who can be helped with neurophysiological therapy? The simple answer is—anyone who has a brain. The program I follow gives people handles to improve the brain in non-invasive ways. If I am able to detect a problem in the neurological exam that I do when I first see my clients, and the family works faithfully with the program I recommend, we almost always see positive change. And the reason for that is simple. When we go back to the way God has created us and programmed our bodies and minds to work, using the laws He has already put into place—healing results.

As we move our bodies, messages are triggered to the brain that bring about change. Our muscles and joints cannot move without the brain, and the brain cannot develop without muscle/joint action.

When an accident happens to your child, it is good to take him to a chiropractor soon. Depending on the stage of development the child is in, the impact of the accident can be more or less major. It is important to go for help at the right time.

Svea Gold, who instructed me, told me that neurologically damaged children invite abuse with their helpless ways and mannerisms. I find that the story is the same for the socially damaged child. Why is it that human nature responds to its weakened members like chickens do— by attacking them?

The uncertain manner that usually accompanies neurologically damaged children stems from the fact that they are not comfortable with who they are. As eye control and coordination improve, their whole outlook changes and a confident manner appears. And they step out to be whole people. I love to watch that happen.

Touch is extremely important for children. If they are not being touched by their parents, they will become hyper, running into walls and acting crazy. They do this to get sensory input, and are trying out possibilities to feel touch. Massage your child on his legs, arms and back—and you will aid his development.

You will also stimulate his cranial nerves by rubbing his head. I remember watching a father hold his child one Sunday afternoon while we were visiting. He was rubbing his baby gently across his head, just as we teach parents to do in one of the exercises we use. Then I recalled that this family had brought one of their older children to see me ten years ago. Not only was he rubbing his child's head as parents do without being taught, he had refined the skill from his previous experience.

There are many ways you can help your child develop his speech. Tummy time on the floor as a small infant is extremely important for this. Put your newborn on his tummy, and he will become accustomed to the position that will help his neurological development. If you wait too long, the baby will not like the position. It is also important that the baby experiences different textures in his mouth by the time he is five or six months old. Babies must put toys and food into their mouths. A baby who doesn't eat well will probably have difficulty with speech.

When I work with abused clients, I use a program that proceeds very slowly. Abuse stops the normal neurological development of the child at the age at which the abuse occurs. You often hear this in the high-pitched voices traumatized individuals use. The more childish the voice is, the earlier in their history the abuse probably occurred.

Primitive reflexes are developed in utero, and children need them for the first six months of their lives. But if they do not integrate, they will keep other more mature reflexes from developing.

I know a child has retained reflexes if I see the following:
- A two-year-old startling easily. A child cannot express feelings until this disappears.

- A sucking reflex that is not gone by nine months.

- A four-year-old who puts things in his mouth. This is a throwback to the reflexes that helped the child to nurse.

- A child wetting himself during the day, but not at night. Wearing sweat pants will help keep a boy dry while you work to integrate the spinal gallant reflex.

- A child who does not walk until he is seventeen to eighteen months old.

- A child lacking in good posture and unable to move one limb at a time.

When a student has trouble with math, he often has improper eye dominance. If you want to increase your child's comprehension and math skills, let the child walk up a safe set of stairs with his eyes shut.

I routinely check to see if babies were nursed or bottle-fed. Babies establish eye dominance on the side that is closest to the mother's body. The eye on that side will be near sighted, while the other will be far sighted. If you are using a bottle, make sure you switch from left to right in the same way you would if you were nursing.

We have many children (and adults) who are stuck in the "terrible two" stage. This happens when the brain struggles as one side tries to lead. When no dominance takes place, the brain is frustrated, and the child is stuck at a distressed level.

If the child is not able to use both sides of his brain, we are also in trouble. Then he will be stuck at the toddler stage, where he will react in fear and anger. He will react to making mistakes, and will be afraid of failing. Neither will he express himself well.

Adults who operate on the maturity level of a child should address these issues—because they can be helped.

Ear infections can change ear dominance. Be aware of which ear your child turns toward you after he has had an ear infection.

There are also situations where the child should have more emotional bonding time. This child's drawing and writing may be poor, though it is apparent that intelligence is present. What the child lacks is the emotional and physical ability to peruse that intelligence.

🪢 🪢 🪢

I am glad to help children where they can't fit in and life isn't working. Among the thousands of cases I have handled, there have been many interesting ones. I will share a few of them with you.

Rodney came to me when he was thirteen years old. He could not make eye contact, and he handled change very poorly. Rodney was hyperactive and controlled by fear. (People who cannot see properly will be more hyperactive. It becomes difficult to contain yourself when you can't focus with your eyes.)

As we discussed Rodney's case, I learned that he had been a bright, happy toddler. When he was three, he had been hit by a baseball above the right eye. At that point his personality shifted, and he lost his humor. His development dropped off sharply. But he loved animals. He found companionship with his chickens and his dog.

Rodney was blessed with committed parents. They stuck faithfully with the program I designed. We saw a marked change in Rodney within the first three months. Over the next months, change came gradually until I discharged him twenty months later. Rodney can now talk with ease, and he meets the eyes of others with a sparkle in his own. His good humor has returned, and he has been able to fit in with others much like an average person. His parents call me from time to time and tell me that Rodney is enjoying a productive life.

✼✼✼ ✼✼✼ ✼✼✼

I remember another family who brought their eighteen-month-old child to me. Brian could not sit up. He did not even have the skills of a three-month-old infant. As he lay quietly on a blanket before me, I listened to the story of his life. Brian had had heart surgery when he was three weeks old. During the surgery, his brain bled—leaving his right side totally useless.

The father looked at me with pain in his eyes. "Joan," he asked, "Will our baby ever walk or talk?"

I looked at Brian, and my heart asked the same questions. But I remembered similar cases where we had seen beautiful results.

"I'm not God," I said. "But I see possibilities, if you are willing to work hard."

"We'll do anything you say," he answered confidently.

So we began a very intensive exercise program. The parents did one round of therapy a day, while the community stepped in to do two more. Brian started waking up. Within a year he was rolling across the floor on his own, playing with toys.

Finally after a year and a half, Brian's father called me. "Joan," he said, "we're almost burned out from working so hard on Brian's program. And the community is too. Can we stop?"

"Yes," I answered. "Go ahead and stop the program. But keep on doing backward lizards. That will help Brian to maintain the improvement he has gained."

This fall, Brian will go to school in a normal first-grade classroom. Has it been worth the work and effort? Brian and his family are delighted, and my heart rejoices!

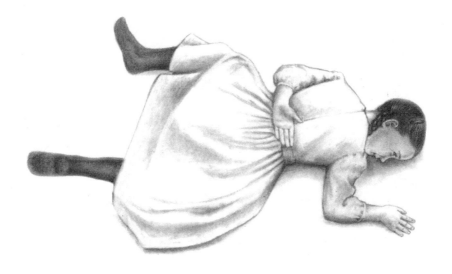

Amber, a third grader, was right dominant except for her left-handedness. She was having trouble coping socially, and she struggled desperately to do her school work. As I worked with her, I learned from her mother that she had burned her arm and hand when she was eighteen months old, when her hand dominance was being established.

When we began teaching Amber to use her right hand, she was very uncomfortable with the procedure. She became angry, would not listen, and was irritable. However, we insisted. The mother stuck with the program. At the end of two months, Amber came to me beaming. We had had a breakthrough! She had made the switch in her brain, which was now able to function without constant static. School work was becoming easier, and Amber was making more friends. Life was on the rise for her again.

※※ ※※ ※※

I remember Lavern, an unhappy third grader, who came into my office with reading problems. During the neurological exam, I asked Lavern if he could read for me a bit.

"No!" the little boy said, "I will not read to you!"

"Surely, " I said smoothly, "you could read for me a little bit, couldn't you? I will help you if you get stuck."

"No," he said, "I can't read to you!" Then Lavern burst into tears.

I gave him a bit of time to recover. Then I asked. "What happens when you read, Lavern?"

"I always get a ter'bal headache when I read," he said, as he looked at me warily.

"That must be bad," I acknowledged kindly. "But if you let me see what happens when you read, maybe I can help you fix the problem."

He finally conceded. I helped him read three sentences from a first grade reader. As he did so, the words were labored and halted. His eyes were focusing very poorly, and were dull by the time he was done. We put Lavern on thirty minutes of therapy per day, with most of it strengthening his eye muscles and teaching his eyes to work well together.

Three months later my little boy came running in the walk to my office and straight into my therapy room. His eyes were beaming as he parked himself in front of me, exclaiming, "Joan, I love to read!"

"What, Lavern?" I asked. "The last time you were here, you hated to read because you got a headache."

"Reading is fun now!" Lavern laughed as he shared his joy with me. "The headaches went away."

Would anyone wonder why I love my job?

※ ※ ※

Adrian was a precious three-year-old with very crossed eyes and extremely poor coordination. He wore glasses. However, when he came into my office for his six-week checkup, his glasses were gone. His mother explained that since he was doing his exercises, he could see better without the glasses. I looked at the little boy. His eyes were indeed functioning together. There was no more crossing.

"He loves his exercises," his mother said, smiling, "and he feels so much better when he does them. If I would let him, he would do them two times a day."

Jonathan was a sixth grader doing fourth-grade work who came to me with problems in spelling and reading. School was a drudgery for everyone involved. But after seven months of therapy, he bounced into my therapy room with delight written on every feature of his face.

His mother looked at me with tears in her eyes. "Jonathan has caught up two grade levels in the past seven months," she explained. "He loves to read and looks forward to school every day."

"My therapy makes me feel so good, I don't want to miss a day of exercises!" Jonathan exclaimed.

Then I think of the mother who hugged me as she left my office. "Joan," she spoke softly, "you have given us hope." Then she added shyly, "You know what? It is fun being a parent now. We all are so much less frustrated than we were three months ago. How can I thank you enough?"

Caleb came to me as he was approaching school age. His mother knew something was wrong because he routinely ran into the sharp corners of doorways. As I examined him, I found that he had vision problems. The reason he was running into things was because he saw two of everything. When we corrected his vision with therapy, that problem—as well as many others—disappeared.

Hannah was a little girl who frequently fell for no apparent reason. She told her father that she would fall asleep walking, and wake up lying on the ground. It was especially bad when these episodes happened while she was going up or down steps. We did therapy with Hannah for two years, and the seizures she was experiencing disappeared. She has been free of seizures for years now.

Do you wonder that I love watching my children succeed? And to see their families find rest? Every day of working with them is a joy. And when I commit my children to God as I go to bed at night, I thank God for giving me the wonderful opportunity of making a difference in the lives of children. What could be better?

God's heart is always with His children. He knows the purpose He has in mind for the life of each child that is born—and the greater purpose of that life for eternity. Jesus said, *"Suffer little children, and forbid them not, to come unto me: for of such is the kingdom of heaven"* (Matthew 19:14). May we tenderly nourish the little ones God places in our care!

chapter seven

The First Two Years and Their Developmental Stages

If there is one thing we would like to say one hundred times in this book, it is PUT YOUR BABY ON THE FLOOR! A clean mat on the floor is a wonderful place for a baby to explore the world and discover himself. Forget the charming jump seats, infant seats and walkers—which all suppress the natural development of your child. Natural movements are necessary for healthy neurological development to take place. Within the first year of his life, a baby lays the neurological groundwork from which his future development and intellect will expand.

A newborn enters the world with a brain that is largely undeveloped. Although the miracle of the human brain develops rapidly before the baby is born, he arrives with skills aimed largely at survival. A newborn makes movements based on reflexive, automatic responses. If you stroke his right cheek, he will turn his head in that direction to search for milk. If he is frightened, his response is based on another reflex to sound an alarm that aids his survival.

As the baby grows in the womb, enters the world as a newborn, and develops throughout childhood, intricate, controlling sets of reflexes move into position, and then recede again, until the individual reaches maturity in each level. When these steps cannot take place at the proper time, we have damaged children who cannot function normally.

As the baby lies on the floor on his stomach, he learns to manage neck and head control outside the warm, supporting fluids of the womb. He must now deal seriously with gravity. As he does this, he is practicing balance, increasing his muscle tone, and developing abilities that relate to the sense of touch. The potential to develop speech at a later time is also shaping now.

Having the baby's head in proper alignment with the rest of his body is necessary for eye tracking, processing sound, muscle tone and organized movements. He will need all of these so that he can later focus and pay attention in school and in his work.

You will want to give your baby both "tummy time" on the floor and time on his back. He will learn to support his head and upper shoulders when he is on his stomach. He also needs the opportunity to kick as he exercises his arms and legs. When you see him putting his big toe into his mouth, you will know that he is learning that his foot belongs to him.

A child learns with his mouth. Put colorful toys before him that he can learn to grasp and put into his mouth. Later put them a little farther away so that he will creep forward on his stomach to reach them.

By the time the baby is two or three months old, he should be rolling from his side to his back, and learning to reach for small toys. He should also be able to push his feet down on a flat surface when you hold him in an upright position.

In the next three months, the baby learns to reach for specific items, to sit with some support, and to roll over from his back to his side. Most babies begin creeping on their stomachs when they are about four or five months old. At about the same time, babies begin using their entire hands to grasp objects.

If the baby is developing normally, he should be able to sit without support by the time he is six to seven months of age. At about the same time, he should babble and be interactive with others. He should begin to crawl on his hands and knees at about six to seven months. By eight months, most babies can pull themselves to a standing position, At nine months, the ability to hold an object between the thumb and forefinger develops. By ten to eleven months of age, most babies will stand alone for a short period of time. Children can begin feeding themselves, with poor aim, at about ten to twelve months.

As the baby moves, he stimulates his brain, which is then able to grow nerve nets and connections upon which his future ability to perform will depend.

Yes... put your baby on the floor. Give him bright toys, and sometimes get down on the floor to play with him. Talk to him as you go about your daily work. Pick him up and take him with you as you do things. Smile into his eyes. Rock him. Hug him, and toss him into the air (with reasonable care, as he gets older). And read stories to him long before you think he can comprehend them. You are the coach who is developing your baby's neurological development!

❋ ❋ ❋

If a child is to accomplish everything that needs to happen within the brain during the crawling stage, he should crawl for at least four to five months. As a child crawls, many things take shape. This is the time for the left and right sides of the brain to learn to work together, which is a very critical stage of development. If your child does not naturally crawl properly on his hands and knees, coach him until he is able to do so.

We have discussed the importance of the baby spending time on the floor. We begin that by placing a blanket on the floor when our babies are tiny infants, where they learn to strengthen their neck muscles and lift their heads. Then they learn to play in that position. This will also ready the baby to crawl properly when the time for that stage comes.

If your baby is eight months old and has not learned to crawl on his own, you can prop a smooth table board against a hassock, put the baby on top, and slide him downward while you work his arms and legs. Another way is to put the child on his tummy on a linoleum floor, with a toy in front of him. Then lift his trunk, bend his legs, and move his arms and legs. (It works best to have two people to do these exercises.)

My doctor once asked me if I had a clue about all the learning disabilities that were developing.

"Yes," I answered, "I can tell you how some of the problem began. When I was still teaching school, doctors began telling parents to put their children to sleep on their backs. And I said, 'We are in for trouble. Six years from now we are going to have a whole new raft of learning disabilities.' My co-teachers wondered why I said that.

"You know what babies do when we put them on their tummies," I continued. "They lift their heads and look around. When we put them on their backs to sleep, they startle and are frightened. But there is nothing to hold onto, and they are not able to lift their heads. A baby who sleeps on his tummy will crawl much sooner. But if these children do not crawl before they are eight or nine months old, look at all the development that won't happen."

My good doctor looked me with grave concern written on his

features. "Do you mean that we, as doctors, have done this? How can we reverse that?"

"Please," I answered, "encourage parents to give their babies tummy time from the first day."

A baby who has not learned to lift his head from the blanketed floor on which he is lying will not like to lie on his tummy. And if he does not like to lie on his tummy by the age of three months, he is not going to learn to crawl in time to finish all the work of that time period. It is much easier to get a baby to crawl properly when he is tiny than it is to undo the damage after he is in school, suffering the consequences of not having crawled.

Our children also have problems when they are high-strung neurologically. They may be rolling at two to three months, crawling at five months and walking at eight or nine months. Neither are they cuddly. The problem is that they are operating in the fight-or-flight mode. They cannot relax, or even become vulnerable to being hugged with comfort. They are always "running from the tiger." Therefore they become demanding children who feel the need to be in control in life, and with their parents.

With these children, I address the retained reflexes that signal fear. Then the children are able to relax and become carefree children, and normal discipline can be used to bring good results.

⁂ ⁂ ⁂

Wanita called me after her son's absentmindedness became frustrating. We discussed the problem. Wayne was now nine years old and at the top of his class. But it was difficult for him to finish jobs, and he had some speech problems.

"I read your article, Edith, and I wondered if you could help my

103

son," Wanita continued. "He never crawled. Could that be causing the problem?"

"It's certainly possible," I replied.

"Is that what is causing his speech problem, too?" she asked.

I pondered for a moment. "When your son was an infant, did he spend time on his tummy?" I asked.

"No, he didn't," she said.

"We're probably seeing results from that too," I answered. "When a child does not spend time on his tummy, and does not crawl, the brain isn't able to wire itself properly. A baby's speech develops when he puts things into his mouth, and when he lies on his tummy—lifting his head and strengthening his neck muscles. But we can still work on all the problems he's having now. And the sooner we start, the more receptive his brain will be to forming new nerve nets and connections."

It was a delight to work with Wayne. A year after he started the program, he was ready to be discharged.

"I just can't believe the difference in Wayne," his mother smiled. "His life is... so much more put together now. And we're so grateful."

※ ※ ※

The normal development of a child is beautiful, and one we tend to take for granted—until we see problems in our children. If we are willing to learn the things that we can do to help our children develop in a healthy manner at the optimum time, we give our children the best advantages for life as competent persons.

Many things assault our children's development today. But help is available. By repeating the same type of motions that were missed as a child developed, we can form connections and central nervous system developments that will help the child to move forward and bloom.

Injuries and emotional trauma may also reactivate reflexes that were previously integrated. The sooner a parent begins to find help for his neurologically-challenged child, the more efficient his development will be. Whereas the human brain can change as long as there is life, the most help can be achieved by working with the individual at the youngest age possible.

Ways to Help our Infants Develop Proper Neurological Pathways

The vestibular development of a baby occurs in the last two months of a normal pregnancy. If you were on bed-rest at this point of your pregnancy, or are the mother of a preemie, there are a few simple things that you will want to know. You can help your baby catch up by very gently twisting and turning his body. As you nurse the baby, sit on an office chair and go back and forth very slowly and gently, from left to right and back again.

If your baby was born C-section, he has missed an important body mapping event. Compensate for this by wrapping him snugly in a soft blanket. Hold him firmly in your arms. And don't forget to do ample amounts of rubbing his back, his tiny arms, legs, feet and hands, and his fingers and toes. Very gently stimulate his scalp, ears and face. Our brains create maps of where the parts of our bodies are as they receive the stimulation of touch.

Making eye contact with our babies is serious business. Babies are born looking for faces and eyes with which to make contact and connections. They can tell by the gentle, intense glow that dances in our own eyes that we love and accept them. It is possible to give a worthless smile with our lips while our eyes contradict the message. But when we care, our delight is written in our eyes.

Where do we look when we are talking to someone? By some principle that science cannot explain, our eyes show the inventories of our souls. A baby knows that from Day One. Have you ever noticed how a baby searches for eyes to meet as he looks around a room, and lets his gaze linger when he finds a face? Babies trust some people immediately, while they withdraw from others.

Babies thrive when they see joy in their mothers' eyes, with the unspoken message that says, "I love you, Treasure! I am delighted to be with you." When a baby does not look into eyes that are full of joy, they become filled with fear and cannot attach emotionally. They will find it hard to recover from situations that cause emotional pain, and will mistrust people in general.

This affects the joy center in the brain, where a child's emotional stability is determined. As he searches his parent's eyes, he knows if his parent is indifferent to him, or if his parent is frustrated and angry. When he sees love-filled eyes, the joy center of his brain, located in the right, orbital pre-frontal cortex, fills in its data base with messages that form the substance of personal security.

Bonding, which is extremely important in the first two years of a child's life, also takes place in the joy center of the brain. If a child bonds well with his mother, and later his father, a sure foundation is put into place for his future neurological development. The same gifting to a child determines the ease or difficulty the child will have in becoming a secure, trusting individual who will be able to nurture wholesome, mature relationships.

Physical touch is a necessary part of nurture for our babies. Through physical touch, children are able to develop a wholesome awareness of who they are as persons. Massaging your baby will help to develop a good body map, and is necessary if he is to know where he is in space. Play little finger games that go with rhymes. Rubbing a child's head gently will help to develop the processing part of the brain. And rubbing his back will calm him.

Rocking a child in a rocking chair is extremely important in developing the vestibular part of the brain. You can also swing children in a circle around yourself. However, stop when your arms get tired, because too much stimulation will turn off part of the brain. For this reason, I discourage infant swings that can be set to stay in motion indefinitely. Using them can damage a child neurologically.

Tummy time is extremely important for developing good upper trunk and neck control for good speech, and for setting the stage so that the baby will crawl at the right time for about four to five months. Tummy time also helps develop hip muscles that will be needed when he walks, and eye muscles that will be necessary if he is to read well later.

A child needs interaction with his father for many reasons. One of these is the kind of play fathers instinctively do without being coached, when they throw their children upward into the air, and twirl them. Within the bounds of sensible reason, this is good for a baby's development.

Use lots of activities that cross the midline. (By that we mean reaching to the right side with the left hand, and so on.) Teaching a child to pat-a-cake is far more than a traditional little game. This activity helps to wire the brain correctly. When you give your child Cheerios, scatter them over the high-chair tray. The child will develop hand-eye coordination as he picks them up, as well as developing his tactile (touch) library with more textures.

A very good exercise that builds connections between the two hemispheres of a child's brain is done when you take the right hand and pat the left knee; then take the left hand and pat the right knee. (Alternate the side you start on with your baby by days, starting on the left one day, and on the right the next. Always end with the side you did not begin with. After the child has established a dominant side, always begin with the dominant hand.)

Signs of Developmental Delay

We know that we are dealing with problem issues when a child flinches and startles after he is two months old. If this is not addressed, the child will find it hard to express his emotions, and will live in a fight-or-flight mode—living fearfully.

Another red flag waving is an unstable clinginess or grabbing onto the parent when he is being carried. Because the child's vestibular is not properly developed, he feels unsteady as his parent moves with him. The same child may mind car sickness.

If your child holds himself stiffly and resists being cuddled, he is presenting with sensory issues. Poor eye contact indicates that the child's eyes are neither tracking well or working together efficiently. A child with this issue will have multitudes of issues with which to deal, and many things that he will fear.

Children act the way they feel. So there is usually something wrong when they remain irritable. A child like this may be feeling mental confusion on a daily basis.

We also have a problem when the child cannot hold still, because his brain requires constant stimulation. This includes the children who fall off the chairs they are sitting on. Some of them find it hard to close their eyes when they pray, because they lose the sense of knowing where they are in space when their eyes are shut.

※ ※ ※

As the brain develops, both sides should learn to work equally well. This is one of the tasks that belong to the first two years. We do not want to see children developing brain dominance until they are about one and a half to two and a half years old. I sigh when a mother tells me that her baby consistently uses the same hand, because I know we are in trouble. A baby should use either hand or foot equally well. The dominance issue will continue to resolve until eye dominance is finally established at about six or seven years old.

A few years ago I learned to know a couple over lunch at a meeting for adoptive parents. They had two children, one a little boy who was twelve months old, and the other a nineteen-month-old little girl. As we sat around the table, I noticed that both children were eating with their fingers.

"Bless you for allowing your children to eat with their fingers," I said as I smiled to the mother.

She looked at me with surprise written over her features. "Really?" she laughed. "I was afraid you would think I was a sloppy mother. Why do you say that?"

"Letting a child eat with his fingers helps hand dominance to establish itself naturally," I replied. "It also helps by desensitizing the skin around the mouth, the lips, and the inside of the mouth, so that the child will not have hypersensitivity to touch. Everything that goes into the mouth to be chewed on does this."

While a parent might look at a baby eating with his fingers as very messy, wonderful things are really happening. Playing with food is one of the methods I have used to teach handicapped children. If they did not like the idea of food textures, it was necessary to stick their hands into the food and make them lick the food off their fingers.

The mouth is the baby's chief learning tool. Watch a baby and notice how everything goes into his mouth. If he does not do this, he may become a poor eater and may have delayed speech. Toys, textures, and fingers in the mouth are preparing the way for both functions. If your baby lacks motivation, choose a safe object and put it into the baby's mouth to teach him. When a baby chews on a coffee table, he is a normal, developing child.

From the ages of fifteen months to two years of age, there will be a normal period of development that has been dubbed "the terrible twos." This occurs when the two hemispheres of the child's brain struggle for dominance until one leads. When that doesn't happen, the child becomes stuck in his development and is distressed.

When brain dominance has become established, a baby who has stunted growth may begin to grow physically as well. As the brain's hemispheres merge their act and work together in harmony, the child develops more calmness and is more sure of himself.

If the gap between the two sides of the brain is too big, a child may be very developed in some skills while he lacks others. This is because one side of his brain is too active while the other is asleep. I love when the parents who come to see me recognize this problem in their children at a very young age. We can quickly correct the problem at that point, and the child has fewer years of struggling.

❊ ❊ ❊

Avoid a rigid feeding schedule and feed your baby when he is hungry. The "books" do not know your child. If your child is hungry and you deny him food because the appointed time is still thirty minutes away, his basic sense of being cared for is undermined. A baby receives his sense of security in knowing that his parent is providing for him. To a helpless infant, being fed is one of his most pressing needs.

"I thought I was doing the right thing to feed my baby on a rigid schedule," Marcy sighs. "I sat in the other room and cried while my hungry baby wailed. I didn't know that my best efforts were hurting my child emotionally—besides creating unnecessary discomfort for him. I didn't know that I was building a helpless feeling of worthlessness because his crying didn't bring him the help and comfort for which he was begging."

A baby should know that you are hearing him when he cries. You don't have to do what the child wants. But it is important to let him know that you heard. When your two-month-old cries from his crib, go to him. Lay your hand on his back. Tell him, "Mommy loves you. But you need to lie down and go to sleep."

Talk to babies even before they can understand. The sound of your voice means something even if the child cannot comprehend the words you are speaking. I am a firm believer that babies do understand far more than we realize. I don't usually ask to hold a baby until I have talked to him, introducing myself, with some pleasant interchange. Only after doing those things will I ask the baby if I may hold him. When I approach a baby this way, parents are often amazed that the baby will reach for me. However, if the baby draws back, I will not remove him from his parent's arms. By handling the issue this way, I am teaching the baby that I value him as a person.

Relate to your baby companionably. Remember that the first two years of a child's life are extremely important for the all-important task of bonding. A child whose mother meshes her heart with his own will need much less discipline. You begin this process by being comfortably in charge and setting the pace with a gentle confidence. Then the trusting, supported child will wish to be in harmony with his mother and will delight in following her. The joy center of his brain will be full!

A child who has been gifted in this manner will enter life with a free, happy spirit that enables him to relate to other people as well. And his heart will be open to believe in and receive the tender love of God, which fully embraces His children.

A baby should be the star of his mother's heart, and he belongs on her lap for the first two years of his life. I am always glad when a mother brings her baby along for the evaluation of an older child. A baby should very rarely be left with a sitter until he is two years old, because his bond with his mother is still being established. This contributes greatly to his sense of security.

If you have children who are spaced closely, sometimes hold both babies at the same time—one on each side. And create cuddle time for your older baby who is missing you. What is sometimes described by the term "jealousy" in young children is not as much a carnal response as it is the child desiring what should belong to him.

A closely-spaced child who did not receive adequate emotional support during the first two years of his life tends to feel inadequate and lonely, and may resent his younger sibling. A happy, contented mother will be best equipped to bless both of her babies when they come close together. Our children, like empty sponges, absorb so much from the way we see and approach life.

A small child can be molded in two ways. We can see the analogy in horticulture.

The first method is to care tenderly for the tiny plant, supporting and fertilizing it with care, giving it adequate light and watering conditions—so that it grows beautifully from the start. And it flourishes!

The other is to plant a seed and care for it haphazardly, sometimes overwatering it and sometimes letting the soil dry out. And letting the weeds grow. When you finally rescue a plant like this, pulling the weeds will seriously disturb the tender rootlets. And the plant will be so weak and straggly that you may need to stake it to give it a chance to stand up.

Which way do you wish to raise your child?

Therapeutic Playtime for Infants
  · Stroke the baby's skin with a soft brush to stimulate skin sensation.

  · With the baby on his tummy, gently stroke his upper back and the back of his neck to get him to lift his head.

- Help the baby to prop himself on his elbows (with his arms pointing forward or inward).

- Bring his hands together at midline, making pat-a-cake motions.

- Help him roll over; gently take his legs and roll him onto his side, making sure his arm is positioned in a way that he will not hurt himself. A good position for this would be to put his arms above his head.

- Tie rattles to his feet and hands to help promote movement.

- Have him chew on many different textures to desensitize the mouth, helping to ready him for speech. Try a diaper, your clean finger, or a koosh ball, being careful that the item you choose is clean and safe.

- Talk to your baby! Make faces at him. Wrinkle up your brow, stick out your tongue, purse your lips and so on. You will be surprised how much the baby can imitate you.

- Let him explore your face with his hands.

- Shake bells outside his field of vision to get him to turn his eyes toward the source of sound.

- Introduce strained food from a spoon by six months, since textures in the mouth help develop the parts of the mouth he will need for speech. If you wait too long to introduce different textures, he will receive them with greater resistance.

- With the baby on his tummy, prop a book with bright pictures in front of him. This will help him strengthen those very important upper trunk muscles. (All babies should spend some play time on their tummies, whether they enjoy it or not. Remember that the floor is much more conducive to development in a normal manner than an infant seat, walker, or infant swing.)

· Sit the baby in the corner of a soft chair, propped so he can move his head freely, and play peek-a-boo games with him that require him to move his head from side to side to follow your movement.

· When he is lying on his back, take his hands and gently help him pull himself up. Or with the child seated on your knees, facing you, hold his hands and help him pull himself up to a standing position (making sure you are supporting him adequately). This helps develop the large trunk muscles that are so important for speech later on.

· Help him coo and gurgle by imitating the sounds he makes. He will love the interchange!

· Seat him on your lap facing you, with his legs straddling yours, almost against your chest. Massage down his back. He will arch his back and hold it straight. This helps strengthen those back muscles.

· If the baby has a problem sitting up, prop him in a dishpan surrounded by soft pillows, and allow him to play in this position. Use one of those beanie sitters for infants, or a Bumbo seat, for short times. This allows him to use his muscles more than an infant seat does.

· For a baby who is behind normal development in crawling, hold him in the crawling position with a blanket roll or your arm supporting his abdomen. Help him hold his weight on his arms and legs. Move an arm and then a foot forward for him.

· Using a small beach ball, lay the baby on the top of the ball on his tummy. Gently tip him forward and allow him to play in this position for a bit. Make sure he is supporting himself on at least one of his arms, making sure he alternates arms.

- For the baby whose hands are tightly fisted, open his hands and gently stroke his palms with a soft brush or washcloth. Or get him to grasp toys.

- Lay the baby on his back, with noisy toys hanging within easy reach. Coax him to bat at the toys.

- To help him work his way forward, lay a bright toy just beyond his grasp when he is playing on his tummy.

Ideas to Develop Fine Motor Skills for Older Children
- Put Cheerios on toothpicks.

- Put toothpicks into holes in a spice container.

- String beads. Eventually have the child string beads in a pattern.

- Play in whipped cream. Make roads, lick fingers, and so on.

- Play with play-doh. Pinch it into little pieces, poke holes into it with your finger, roll it into a snake, cut it with a table knife…

- Stack blocks in high towers.

- Hang up washcloths on a clothesline with clothespins.

- Put pegs in a pegboard. You can also work at sorting by color or stacking.

- Fold washcloths.

- Turn the pages of a book one at a time.

- Do coloring. I like to outline the picture heavily in advance. It creates a small ridge to help keep the child's crayon within the lines.

- Spoon dry rice from one bowl to another.

- Use tongs to pick up cotton balls.

- Put paper clips onto paper.

- Sort tiny items (marbles, paper clips, pennies, chocolate chips and so on) into a cupcake tin. Give the child a cup with an assortment of multiples.

- Play with a set of tiny farm animals. Get the child to build pens with his blocks, and then stand the animals in the pens.

- Sort colored toy bears, small animals or objects into the correct colors of bowls.

- Do lots of puzzles.

- Drop flat marbles or other small objects into a narrow-necked bottle.

- Play doll with a set of tiny dolls. Make them ride horses or go to bed. Cover them with a blanket and so on.

- Create masking tape roads on the floor to step along, or to drive matchbox vehicles on.

- Use popsicle sticks to stick into play-doh, and pull them out again.

- Lots of pretend play is good. Have tea parties for the dolls and teddy bears. Make play-doh cookies for them. Practice feeding the dolls and teddy bears.

- Teach the child to open a padlock with a tiny key.

- Have him try to tie a string around a crayon.

- Let him put a rubber band around a stack of picture cards.

- Pour water from one cup into another.

Use your imagination for more…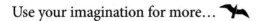

chapter eight

The School Years

School adds a broadening dimension to a child's life. He learns academically as he becomes acquainted with numbers and letters, and socially as he interacts with his classmates. The playground is a great place for learning to get along with others.

Encourage a positive attitude toward school in your child. Understand the difficulties he may face with his classmates. Children are not always kind. Show him that school is important to you by visiting and by asking him questions. Hang a worksheet that was done with his best effort on your refrigerator for everyone to see—and add your own gold star. You might also play games that use numbers or words that he is learning at school.

It lends harmony to a parent/teacher relationship when both parties give the other the benefit of the doubt. If we realize that we are not going to be perfect in our roles at home, it will help if we extend the same kind of gracious acceptance to the teachers of our children. Working together with love for the child will make our work effective and bless the children we love.

It is wise to remember that what happens at home will affect school the next day. A traumatic evening or a short night will color the next school day. And a stressful school day will also spread ripples into your home when your child enters the kitchen door with his empty lunch box. The home and the school can best complement the child's opportunity to learn by working together with mutual respect.

Teach your child to be socially acceptable and to fit in as normally as possible with his classmates. Practice with him to stop and pay attention when people talk to him, and to reply politely. "Good morning," "Excuse me, please," and "Thank you" are pleasant words that lubricate relationships.

He should know to wipe his own nose and to cover his mouth when he coughs. Coach him on boundaries so that he knows how much and where it is permissible to touch other people. Many special children cannot understand body language and personal space.

There are some things your child's teacher should know. What about your daughter's cycling? Is your child on medication for any reason? Does he get seizures? If so, what should the teacher do?

Life skills can be addressed both at home and in the special-ed classroom. This would include teaching the child to brush his teeth, to get his clothes pulled up properly in the bathroom, and to tuck in his shirt tail. Does he wash his hands before he leaves the bathroom? If the child drools, teach him to stop and think, and then to swallow his saliva.

One of my little boys responded well to the simple directive, "Find your resting place, Randall." It was my cue to remind him to close his mouth and swallow. Gradually he learned to catch himself before he began drooling.

Table manners can also be addressed. Does the child chew with his mouth open? What about the volume of his voice? Does the child need help to keep his hands to himself, and not to lean too close to other people?

There are things special-ed teachers would be happy to assist parents with at school, if they knew their help would be appreciated. One child needed lots of help learning to dress. So his mother sent his everyday clothing along to school, and we worked at dressing skills in the last few minutes of the day. A teacher might also help the child learn to tie his shoes or to use a safety pin.

✾ ✾ ✾

Specifics about Dyslexia

Most of the reading part of the brain is in the back. The dyslexic has a glitch that does not allow him to access this center. The reading center in the front part of the brain, which he uses, is less efficient. It will only be able to sustain a much slower reading rate.

One of the good books that are available on dyslexia is **Overcoming Dyslexia,** by Sally Shaywitz, M.D. Being personally informed prepares a parent to work for his child's welfare. If your school board and teacher do not have a working understanding of dyslexia, I encourage parents to offer to share good information with them. Do this in an objective, calm way. The father of the child is very important in this process. Many people will wish to be supportive if they are given the facts.

It is important for parents, teachers and school boards to be aware of curriculum that is specifically designed for dyslexic students. Having the right curriculum makes everything work better. One of the very good reading curriculums available is the Barton program.

In general, an early-intervention dyslexic reading program should include the following:

Systematic and direct instruction in:
- phonemic awareness (taking notice of, identifying, and working with the sound of spoken language).

- phonics (learning how letters and letter groups represent the sounds of spoken language).

- decoding (sounding out words).

- spelling.

- reading sight words.

- vocabulary and concepts.

- reading comprehension strategies.

Practice in using these skills in reading and writing.

Fluency training.

Enriched language exercises (listening to, talking about and telling stories).

Trying to get a dyslexic child across the learning curve to being able to read with a traditional curriculum is like trying to pound a square peg into a round hole. So the teacher is less frustrated when she has curriculum that the child is able to relate to. And so is the child. He is delighted when he finds that there is a way to read the letters and words that had been so elusive!

It is important to intervene for the dyslexic child as soon as the problem is observed. That way the brain can more efficiently build new pathways. Recent research, using brain scans of children reading, shows that a dyslexic child's brain changes after he is on a dyslexic reading program for a length of time. The brain establishes new connections that become more like the normal reading functions of the brain.

Math U See is helpful for children who need a similar approach to learning math. *Semple Math* is another good choice.

Reaching the Next Mountain...

The motivation we have to help our children progress will affect the way we support our teachers when they are working to teach new skills. Are you willing to move with your child to the next step? For example, instead of feeding Johnny when you think he should be able to feed himself, caregivers are wise to require him to feed himself for several bites when he is hungry. Then let him do a few more bites on his own each time, as he masters the skill of feeding himself.

Rebecca was asked to move into the family home of a special child, Joseph, to be in charge of teaching him and assisting with his care. She noticed that the skills he had mastered should have enabled him to learn to feed himself. Yet, at meal time, he would squeal and look at his mother, looking much like a hungry, immature bluebird.

When Rebecca was given responsibility for Joseph at meal time, she decided to make Joseph wish to feed himself. So she frequently waited for fifteen seconds before she lifted the spoon to his mouth. And instead of bringing the spoon neatly into his mouth, she sometimes brought the loaded spoon against his cheek, or to the edge of his mouth. Joseph became uncomfortable—and a bit upset. By the fifth meal, Joseph grabbed the spoon from Rebecca's hand and attempted to feed himself. In a few days he was doing a good job.

When you are teaching your child to use a stairway, don't force him to use one foot and then the other for each stair step if it frightens him. But encourage him to try. And be there to catch him if he does fall. You might say, "Look! This is the way I go up the stairs," as you are demonstrating. Then ask brightly, "Can you do that?" Model, invite and encourage new steps of development.

Special children develop deep attachments to things they love. It could be the stuffed animal April sleeps with, a book Terry loves, or the obsessive devotion Crystal has to one aunt. Matthew seldom tires of collecting ladybugs.

When these obsessions do not interfere with normal daily life, allow your child to enjoy his interest, since it brings him a measure of comfort. However, you can limit the places that stuffed animals may go, and put them away during family devotions or at meal times. Or you can say that we have collected enough ladybugs for one evening. Parents will need to draw the line in their own homes.

Dealing with Problem Issues

Sometimes you will notice puzzling issues in the way your children present.

I remember a situation like that with Wayne, one of my special-ed students. Wayne passionately loved his grandfather, who walked with a limp. He often spent several hours on Sunday afternoon with his grandfather.

It became a habit that Wayne would walk into school on Monday morning with a limp. He would hobble into the room on those mornings, muttering, "Foot hurt." And then a gratified martyr-like look would come over his face. Sometimes, when I took his shoe off to investigate, a small stone would fall out.

"Watch out for stones, Wayne," I would say. "They don't feel good in your shoe." He would nod with a very important look on his face.

Yet nothing was consistent. Wayne had no problem walking or doing his form of running when he wanted to get somewhere in a hurry. And the limping problem was usually isolated to Monday mornings. What kind of desire was Wayne trying to fill? How could I help him to meet it a better way?

The following Monday morning, when I took off his shoe, a screw rolled out. I winced when I saw the red area the screw had aggravated. And a light dawned in my mind when I heard Wayne's next comment. "Foot hurt," he moaned piteously. "Big man—like Grandpa."

"Wayne," I said, as I stifled a laugh. "I know what you need. You need a cane, just like Grandpa has. We have one at my house. I'll bring it for you to use tomorrow. Would you like to play with it at recess time?" And the boy's face glowed with pleasure.

The cane worked better than putting items into Wayne's shoe had. We were meeting a safety issue so that he would not self-injure his foot. And it took less time to get the cane out of the classroom closet than it had taken to take off his shoes and look for stones—or screws. I allowed Wayne to use the cane only at recess, which brought him great joy. In a few weeks the mood passed, and he only asked for the cane on rare occasions.

These types of situations will occur at home and at school. Be creative and inventive. When you can humor the child in a way that is safe and not disruptive to those around him, it sometimes satisfies him and diffuses a problem situation.

Safety Issues, Record Keeping, Etc.

It is important to talk to your child's teacher when your child brings home stories about accidents that happened at school. And if the child acts strange when he comes home in the afternoon, cries, or doesn't want to go to school, check again. That is the way Rhonda and the teacher found out that Jonathan was being bullied on the playground—and actually hurt—by three older boys. But by working on the problem together, it was soon mended.

There are also times when the handicapped child becomes a bully at school. Be alert so that you can work for the good of the whole class.

Encourage children to guard their own moral purity. Advise your children to tell you if someone is making them uncomfortable by touching them inappropriately. Every four-year-old should be told that there are okay places for other people to touch us and places that are not okay. They should know that the areas of the body that a T-shirt and underwear cover are our private places.

If your child is afraid of any type of caregiver, look seriously at what could be taking place. Fear in the child's experience raises a red flag that warrants concern.

Every child has a tender heart that suffers bumps and bruises from the hurts of life. As adults, we still recall the sharp, hurtful situations of our own childhoods. We can again feel the pain of being rejected as our playmates hid from us; the lost, lonely, unfairness of being accused of stealing candy when no one protected us. As we meet similar situations in our own children's experiences, those memories can return to the surface, clouding our judgment and limiting our effectiveness to help.

Keep a running record of things that impact your child at school, in the event that they will give you and his teacher helpful information in the future. This would include experimentation with different curriculums, social situations that did or did not work, plans for coping with seizures, and etc.

❊ ❊ ❊

Many children start school at the age of six. To be ready for school, a child needs to be ready socially, emotionally and academically. Many children are not ready in all three areas until they are six and a half years old. Girls tend to be ready when their sixth birthday comes, whereas boys often develop the same maturity when they are six months past their sixth birthday. But by the time the class reaches sixth grade, the boys pull ahead of the girls in maturity.

NOTES FOR SPECIAL-ED TEACHERS

Understanding the Child

As we work with special children, we seek to understand the child himself. We are attempting to teach the child life skills and academic values. We are also helping the child develop self-control, character and acceptance of submission.

Our children will showcase emotions or strong feelings with complex reactions that will have both physical and mental manifestations. We will see them process love, hate, fear and anger. As we help our children focus and respond in God-honoring healthy ways, we will talk to them, touch them and care for them in a manner that embraces their total person.

It is important to remember that our children are accountable to parents and caregivers. They are not yet accountable to God. Some of our children will never reach personal accountability and will enter heaven in the same way a small child does. Avoid producing personal guilt in these "little ones."

As I worked with my special-ed students, I learned that the manner in which I acted and presented myself did quite a bit to determine my student's responses to me. If the child sensed that I truly loved him, he was likely to want to please me. To accomplish this, I focused on being comfortable with who the child really was. And when I sensed that he was doing his best, I affirmed him for his hard work. Having won the heart of my child made discipline many times more effective. Children see through us to know how we really feel toward them.

A child will mirror the environment in which he is immersed. If he sees fear and chaos, he will become agitated. If he is with adults who exhibit peace and joy, he in turn will be more restful.

Understanding Discipline

As we discipline our children, we work to teach them to stop and think before they act, to think about consequences, and to choose to do the right thing.

We sometimes wonder when the child has crossed the line to deserve punishment. I found that it was usually fairly easy to tell if he felt guilty for what he had done. If your child feels guilty, punish him to clear his conscience. If he does not realize that he has done wrong, take a gentler approach and help him learn what to do the next time. Children generally want to please the caregivers they love.

As we discipline, we need to make sure that we are both fair and gentle. Never wait to administer a punishment until the child can no longer connect the misdemeanor with his punishment.

We will know that we have been successful in teaching our children when they respond in an appropriate manner and learn to do the right thing. A restful, respectful attitude in the child will also indicate that our goal has been reached.

Discipline and behavior management involve much more than the punishment a child receives. Sometimes we will be able to avert bad situations before they have a chance to take place. Give your child a look that signals your displeasure when you see trouble brewing. Sometimes you will distract the child at this point. And in some cases you may reinforce good behavior by saying, "Thank-you for not tripping Johnny as he walks past you, Sally."

Bless your child by teaching him to make good choices in matters that help build positive lives. If Sammy goes from being giddy to feeling flat, teach him to respect others when he is feeling exuberant. And when he is moody, let him sit outside the door until he can smile nicely. When he answers you disrespectfully, give him the opportunity to share his response in a respectful manner. You will be helping to establish a good pattern.

When Sammy came to school, doing nothing right, I assumed that he had had a bad night, or that something stressful was happening at home. And for that day we focused on something he enjoyed. The next day he always did better.

Habitual offenses deserve attention. When my special-ed students did not cooperate with things that I felt they understood, or looked at me to see what I would do after they disobeyed, I knew that it was time to act. Depending on the child's ability and on his offense, I made judgement calls to match the situation. Sometimes I used punishments that were unpleasant, and sometimes I removed privileges.

If you are dealing with a problem situation, involving a special-ed student, where the parents and the school board disagree, consider asking for a third party. Could a member of the ministry become involved? In some cases, would it be wise to obtain a professional's advice?

Building Up the Child

There are some children who meet a challenge and give up very easily. In working with those situations, I found that it was better to help the child take a smaller step in the direction I was trying to lead him, and return to the activity that challenged him later.

There are some children who use immature actions to test our value of their worth, when they feel surrounded with love and understanding. In those cases, we keep on trying. We look for ways to open the child's heart to respect himself, receive love—and blossom. What makes him feel truly loved?

Some children develop phobias because they know something is going to change. Others lose control when things happen without notice. Be wise in the way you handle things. Talk to the child, and let him be near you. I had a student who became distracted if he knew a test was coming. So I just called the test a worksheet, and he did fine. Find out what works, and do it.

Mary was a student who day-dreamed, and did not do well in sticking with her work. I made her accountable with short-term goals. When she finished the work up to a red dot I had made on her paper, she was to bring the paper to me. And when she reached the sixth row, she was allowed to get a drink. With that kind of guidance, she eventually improved.

Model what you want to teach your children in your own life. Then gently, with careful strategies, guide them to think of others and handle life in a wholesome manner.

❅ ❅ ❅

Checklists for Building Concentration Skills

Issues that could be making it hard for a child to concentrate:

- Perhaps he has supersensitive skin, and his clothing tags are bothering him.

- Could he be simply bored because there is nothing that interests him enough to hold and keep his attention?

- What about the amount of sleep he is getting? A child should have 9½ to 11 hours of sleep per night. This is a goal for parents to look at seriously. If the child is extremely tired in school, in a special-ed classroom the teacher might also have the child take a thirty-minute nap.

- Does he have food allergies? They create brain fog.

- Perhaps his pupils do not dilate and constrict like they should. If that is the case, the child sees movement that takes place around him as clearly as he sees the book he is instructed to read. With so much competing stimuli, concentration becomes difficult.

- Does he have auditory perception problems, which keep him from connecting to the messages his ears are presenting to his brain? He may also have supersensitive hearing that causes him to shut down easily when he becomes overly stimulated.

Handles for Building Concentration

· Give the child a private, quiet place in which to work.

· In some cases, children can concentrate better if there is background noise.

· Create small goals. Divide chores and schoolwork into smaller, manageable portions that the child can do—one at a time.

· Using a timer can be a good incentive. Setting the timer for a reasonable amount of time to accomplish a goal may motivate the child. When my slower school students lacked motivation, I found that setting a timer with the goal that they would finish three rows before the buzzer went off worked better than prompting them to have three rows done before recess.

· Sometimes the hyperactive child's need for movement can be met by giving him a wiggle seat. These are called tactile cushions at teacher's stores. Or you can place a weighted blanket on his lap.

· Help the child establish a goal by requiring that one task be finished before he can start doing something else he wants to do.

· Work to inspire the child with a sense of self-confidence. Do this by helping him to understand his limitations and by affirming him as he does his best. We reach a calm center when we are at peace with ourselves. Give him the opportunity to do things he can do well, and commend him for his successes. Success breeds more success.

· Present new concepts in comfortable stages. That way the child is not overwhelmed, and is more likely to feel that he is in control of his situation.

- The message center in the brain is above the dominant ear. If the child is using the non-dominant ear, it will take much longer for a message to sink in. Have the child practice with a PVC pipe phone when he needs to read or memorize something. This enables the brain to function better. <u>Look in the index at the back of this book to find instructions for making your own.</u>

- When the child can no longer function, stop what you are doing. Do cross-lateral marching exercises. It will help to clear the brain for more effective function.

- At times it is good to give the child something he can easily do. Then carry on a conversation with him while he remains busy. This kind of therapy will help to develop concentration.

- Sometimes a simple break, like running around the building, will bring a touch of freshness to the child.

- A mid-morning protein snack helps tremendously. Your child can work on fine motor skills as he helps you get the snack ready. For example, you could shell peanuts, peel an orange, or spread peanut butter on bread or crackers. Have him make a roll-up with sliced meat and cheese.

Daily Activities That Support Physical Therapy
- Teach the child to dress himself.

- Encourage lots of good, healthy outside play.

- Teach him to sit up straight on his chair.

- Teach him to hold a spoon properly.

- Teach him the proper way to hold a pencil.

- Encourage jumping and skipping. A small trampoline can be a good investment for a special-ed school. Children who have trouble sitting still can jump a few minutes—and return refreshed.

- See if the child can walk up the steps backward. Or forward with his eyes shut. Every child should see what the world looks like from an upside-down position.

Helps That Build Communication Between Parents and Teachers

- Encourage communication. I sent a notebook home with my students each day. On its pages I wrote the new things we were working on at school. The mothers returned it, sharing anything unusual that was going on at home, or a particular skill they were working on with the child. By sending it back and forth on a daily basis, we had an easy channel for communication that fostered a wholesome working together.

- Make a phone call at regular intervals.

- Invite the teacher into your home.

- Talk freely about where your child is in his curriculum, what he will be doing next, and so on.

- Reach out in an open, transparent way that will encourage the sharing of new ideas with one another.

I will include the following lists for teachers who may be perusing this book.

Helpful Hints for Teachers (that bless parents)

- Listen with your heart to the parents' concerns about their children.

131

- Don't push academics to the point of stressing the child out.

- If the parents say their child is stressed, hear them and see what you can do about it.

- Keep communication open to the point where a mother will feel free to visit her child in the classroom without causing tension to build up.

- Express appreciation to the parents for what they are doing for their child. It is not an easy thing to have a special-needs child. Sometimes a mother heart longs for someone who also loves the child to share with her.

- Accept your school children as the persons they really are. Parents appreciate when a teacher works to teach the child more skills but remains realistic about the child's actual ability to learn.

- Show love and caring for the child. Knowing that a teacher truly loves the child encourages trust from parents.

- Maintain a joyful attitude as you work in your classroom. That kind of enthusiasm makes a parent's load lighter.

- Ask the parent for specific goals he has for the child in school. This could include practical everyday skills as well as academic ones.

- Once in a while, do something meaningful with the child outside of the classroom. This will gift both the child and the parent.

Become the friend of your patron parents. Take time to talk with them at church. Being genuine yourself will encourage the parents to respond to you in the same manner.

chapter nine

Learning Disabilities

As the Bible teaches us, we are fearfully and wonderfully made. God created each of us as unique persons, each one beautiful in his own way. We are each like a plant climbing a trellis that in turn guides its growth and affects the way it blooms. As we work with our challenged children, whether we are teachers or parents, we come to understand that there are various approaches that can be taken. We learn that the way we interact with the children will in part determine whether or not they will bloom to their full potential.

That disabilities exist is a reality. Only when we honestly acknowledge disabilities will we be able to offer help. A disability is a biological, medical or neurological health issue that hinders an individual in functioning normally in the routines of life.

A blind person, for example, is not able to function in the same way a sighted person can. There are some things that he will not be able to do, and others that he can learn to accomplish in a new way. He should not look upon himself as "damaged" material. Rather, he should focus on learning new skills to accomplish his goals in life.

I appreciate the fact that God made each of us uniquely. Unfortunately we often fail to see the divine fingerprint on our fellow humans, but look upon someone who cannot meet society's standards as being a nuisance, a burden or lacking in value. Within the last century, special education has helped to bring about drastic changes that have broadened the lives of people who at one time would have been institutionalized, isolated, or at the least considered a burden.

Some people hesitate to have their children diagnosed because they fear that it will cause them to be stigmatized. However, knowing what we are dealing with helps us tremendously in being able to meet the needs. As we teach our children to be respectful and accepting of those who struggle with special needs, they learn to respond in positive, loving ways. This character-building task is one that the Christian home and school should be effecting.

If uncomfortable comments are made, we can help the challenged child to respond appropriately.

- He can simply ignore a rude comment and forgive the person who made it.

- He can acknowledge his disability without feeling responsible to explain the cause, as in saying, "Yes, I do stare into space at times. But I don't do it on purpose."

- He can explain his situation, as in saying, "I am a dyslexic, and am unable to read a book well."

Do not baby a child who has a disability. He should be given responsibilities that he is able to do, and be held accountable. Remember that pity and compassion are two different things. Pity gives the child a nickel or a piece of candy, and then discounts him as a person of equal worth. Compassion reaches out with a friendly handshake and acknowledges the individual's worth. Then it welcomes him to be as active as he is able to be in activities.

Sheltering children inappropriately will not teach them to function as independent adults. We should walk beside them, helping them as they accept their losses. As they learn to function within their abilities, they can find meaning and purpose. We are all handicapped in some way. Childhood is the optimal time to teach love, acceptance and respect—which humans continually need to share with one another.

God has made each of us differently. Being open to only one method of handling issues will not necessarily be proactive. When a paper exam is given, offering an oral exam to a dyslexic student offers fairness. Be open minded, and do what works.

Teacher's Responsibility
Teaching in a conventional classroom is fulfilling. However, I feel that teaching children with disabilities is even more rewarding! A teacher sees pain, struggles and tears, and experiences intense emotions with the child and his parents. And when victory is accomplished, there is great reason to celebrate!

Teachers need to understand that the spectrum of symptoms within a disability will vary from child to child. Learn to be creative, inventive and skillful with new approaches. Yet keep the state of things steady and dependable.

Observing these points will enable us to help the child.
  · Help the child connect with others. It is important to be a part of a group, to have friends, to be able to share and make contributions. When children are welcomed into group activities

that are creative and upbuilding, it helps them develop a sense of belonging that connects them to their heritage. In turn, this sense of belonging helps them develop a relationship with God and builds a sense of security.

- Initiate playtime. Vigorous play is important for proper muscle growth, especially in young children. Play is important in developing a child's creative mind and in learning how to interact with others. As they play, children learn how to work together and solve problems.

- Help children develop perseverance. The discipline of practicing things that are hard develops perseverance in the child. This will help him acquire skills in pushing hard to reach a goal. Habits of self-discipline carry over into every other area of life and build the stage for successful adulthood.

- Help students gain mastery over difficulty. Consider it your first priority to provide the child with tools to conquer his present challenge. When he masters that difficulty, he will have a sense of accomplishment that will build motivation and confidence in facing more challenging situations.

- Recognize a student's accomplishments. We are built up and affirmed as valid individuals when others recognize and value the contributions we have made.

Teachers should also be aware of the following responsibilities in the classroom.

- To educate in a way that each student can comprehend, enabling him to learn in the best way possible.

- To research options and find alternate methods if a child is not able to learn with the method that is in place.

- To provide a cheerful, POSITIVE atmosphere for learning.

- To stand for truth and moral responsibility.

- To hold forth high, but achievable, goals. "Hitch your wagon to a star. But don't cry if you can't make it that far."

- To work honorably with parents, encouraging them. Parents and teachers should be partners. Ask your patron parents for their ideas. They know their children better than you do. Share your own ideas, goals and stories. Listen with your heart. Parents often feel very much alone in their job of raising children with learning difficulties. Share with one another the goals and expectations you hold for the child.

Why Diagnose???

Some parents are hesitant to have their children diagnosed, feeling there may be negative repercussions. I share their concern that the child be related to with respect and dignity in his society. The value of being properly diagnosed is that it aids the child, and those around him, in understanding what he is dealing with. A child with a retained spinal gallant reflex will know that he is not bad because he constantly wiggles, makes clumsy moves or cannot perform like his classmates do. I have had many children throw their arms around me and thank me for telling them that they are not retarded.

Fellow students can learn that Franklin is not strange because he needs a special diet, but that he was born with PKU—and cannot eat the same foods they can. Rather we teach our students that this is how God made Franklin, and we will offer other options when we have special foods, so he can help eat something special too.

We often hurt children with disabilities. Don't say these things about your child:

- He inherited it.

- He just has dyslexia.

- I didn't like school either.

- As long as he passes...

- My child doesn't need extra help. He is just lazy and needs to apply himself.

- My child is dumb.

- He'll never amount to much anyway.

- There is no such thing as a disability. It's just that he doesn't have a good teacher.

Dyslexia

How do you know that your child isn't seeing things backward or upside down? Or that he is hearing the words you speak to him, and that the message is not garbled?

There are several kinds of dyslexia, including auditory or visual. Dyslexia is defined as the impaired ability to read, spell and write words despite the ability to see and recognize letters. A dyslexic child is often very intelligent, but finds it hard to fit into a world that sees things differently than the world his own brain interprets.

Dyslexia is a very real problem that the general public often does not comprehend. Some dyslexics see double, leading them to see more dots than a page contains. Words and letters may not remain in fixed positions for the child as he reads. Or the letters that were at the end of a word may jump into the middle of the word. For this reason, dyslexics often manage to grab a few words and guess at the rest because it is their best way of coping.

Reading curriculums that are designed for dyslexics help immensely. Using an auditory training program may also be very helpful to the child. In classes that are not intended to teach reading, it is helpful to the child if someone reads material to him and then writes down his responses.

I was asked to test John when he needed to go through grade one for the fourth time. John just could not learn—or so it seemed. As I tested him with copying designs, he made two of each object and endless rows of dots.

When I played ball with him, he also had trouble catching the ball. "How many balls do you see, John?" I asked.

"There's just one ball," he answered.

"Yes," I said. "But how many do you see, John?"

"Well," he spoke hesitantly, "it looks like there are two."

We talked about reading. He told me that he does not like reading because the words on the page won't stand still so he can read them.

John had a very fearful childhood. As a baby he had screamed and screamed while his mother did not know how to comfort him. He hated going to church or into any large crowds. He was afraid of darkness and shadows, and he would not go to sleep without a night light.

I started John on a program, and in two years' time, he was ready for grade six. John had a sharp mind. After we worked with his dyslexia and other issues, he was able to put things together. Today John is doing well.

If you are dealing with a dyslexic child in a community where the problem is not understood, share information in ways that will be received. One book we recommend is *Overcoming Dyslexia*, by Sally Shaywitz, MD. Most people will become supportive if they are open to learning about the disability.

For lists of symptoms that are typical of a dyslexic, look for the following lists at the end of this chapter: Visual Perception, Visual Perceptual/Visual Motor Deficits and Auditory Perceptual Deficits.

Dyslexia can include the following:

· Delayed speech —We normally expect a child to use single words in the first year, two words together during the second, and mini sentences in the third year.

· Stuttering —Early-onset stuttering, when your child begins forming sentences, is not uncommon. The left side of the brain helps us construct sentences, while the lilt of language and the gaps between the words depend on the right brain. Ninety-eight percent of children with learning disabilities have right-side brain problems. It may be a delay in development that causes this problem. (A PVC pipe "telephone" and joint compression exercises are helpful in addressing this.)

· Recurrent ear infections —When you see middle-ear infections, eczema and asthma, suspect dyslexia. These symptoms often accompany this condition. This should not surprise us since all of the conditions we have mentioned rely on the right side of the brain.

· Poor coordination —While this often accompanies dyslexia, the proper name for poor coordination is dyspraxia. This will be discussed later.

· Confusion over left- or right-handedness. We normally expect the left side of the brain to develop first. This may explain why most people are right-handed.

When a child has difficulty reading, and letters appear to move on the page, he may be experiencing convergence issues. Fifty-eight percent of learning-disabled children have accommodation/convergence failure. That may mean that the child has to look at something from a very close position, since his eyes have to move in toward his nose so he can focus on the word he is reading. Sometimes he will hold his head at an odd angle so he can see the words well enough to read.

In many cases involving learning or behavioral difficulties, one of the eyes fails to converge well. Most of these children would not say that they have double vision. Yet the information the weaker eye supplies must be ignored by the brain. This causes both processing and tracking issues that lead to nystagmus (eyeball jerking). Interestingly, very few opticians test for convergence failure.

You can test for convergence yourself. Hold your pen about 18" in front of the child's face in a centered position. Now move the pen tip toward the child's nose, telling him to look at the pen tip all the time. The eyes should start to move inward at the same time, and they should still be able to look at the pen tip when it is one-half inch from the eye. If an eye delays in beginning to move, moves outward, or comes inward faster than the other, we have a convergence issue.

A few children with dyslexia are hypersensitive to light. Just a quick flash of light during my exam will cause the eyes to stream. This is generally a brain problem that goes along with delayed processing skills.

ADD
The ADD child has difficulty focusing and maintaining attention. He usually has at least six of the following problems.

- Does not pay attention to details and makes careless mistakes.

- Has trouble focusing and maintaining attention.

- Appears not to listen, because he has difficulty blocking out background noises.

- Has trouble completing work.

- Has difficulty with organization.

- Does not enjoy tasks that involve mental function.

- Has trouble keeping up with things.

- Has trouble focusing. On some days he can work well, and on others he is easily distracted.

- Cannot remember important things.

- Cannot multi-task. The child does better doing only one thing at a time.

- Shows contrary behavior.

- Is unpredictable and acts on impulse.

- Often excels in creativity.

- Tends to be irritable, but may have a very tender heart.

- Gives indiscriminately.

- Does not learn from previous mistakes.

The child with ADD often behaves like any other child does—misbehaving, being silly and daydreaming. The difference lies in the extreme or constant nature of the behavioral problem. When the child acts out to the point where it is difficult for him to fit in with his society, we judge it as a problem that should be addressed.

ADHD

For a child to be diagnosed with ADHD, the symptoms must have been present for at least six months, and have developed before the child reached seven years of age. The way the child acts must be incompatible for his age group. Issues stemming from the problems also need to affect two social settings. For instance, the child does not fit in at home or in school. ADHD is suspected when the child is hyperactive, impulsive and inattentive.

Children with ADHD find it hard to sit still, are disruptive and talk excessively. They cannot do things quietly. They are often rough with toys and hurt other children.

The ADHD child will speak and act impulsively. He will try to answer questions before the speaker is done asking his question, and interrupts conversations with inappropriate questions. When the child is frustrated, he will lash out in reactions that are out of proportion to the thing that irritated him.

The frustration that leads to violent outbursts is a clear sign of the hopelessness these children feel but have trouble expressing. They often despise themselves, get into trouble with others and live in a world they cannot understand.

Their thoughts skip around in conversation while the listener is still on a previous subject. One ADHD child said, "It feels like my ideas are like ping pong balls or pop balls, bouncing everywhere." They often have physical energy that is hard to harness.

Some therapists have observed that the symptoms of ADHD are generally comparable to the way a baby functions at one year of age. A one-year-old acts as he does because his brain is still undeveloped, and because the parts of his brain are not fully connected. As I work with children who exhibit ADHD tendencies, I see the symptoms disappearing as we work to bring the brain to fuller development.

Helpful Handles for Children with ADHD
· Set a timer for them.

- Provide lots of encouragement. These children often get themselves into difficult situations, and feel very bad about it.

- Give them extra breaks, rather than simply pushing them to keep at their work.

- Stop and play pitch and catch with them for a break.

- Make sure they get enough sleep.

- Encourage exercise, which is a wonderful antidote. When they get frustrated, give them the opportunity to run hard for a few minutes.

- Offer to be a mentor with an understanding heart. Talking with someone who understands helps them relate to themselves in a more positive way.

- Offer a quiet work zone. When there is less to compete for their attention, they are able to better focus on their work.

Dyspraxia

This term is used to describe children with developmental/learning disabilities, and is often confused with dyslexia.

Children with dyspraxia have difficulty with coordinated acts. (At one point this condition was called the clumsy child syndrome.) For the child, it means that tying shoes, feeding himself and riding a bike are tremendous challenges. Because the child does not know where he is in space, he constantly bumps into and drops things.

Dyspraxia may include the following:
- Has trouble with poor balance.

- Has difficulty doing tasks that require both fine (writing or painting) and gross (running, jumping) motor skills.

- Suffers with poor vision.

- Has difficulty with poor motor planning and perception.

- Does not know where he is in space.

- Has trouble reading, writing and speaking.

- Has trouble relating socially.

- Exhibits emotional/behavioral problems.

Have you noticed the areas of overlap between developmental dyspraxia and dyslexia?

It is the right side of the brain that deals with your position in space. In 98 percent of children with developmental problems, we find that the development of the right side of the brain is delayed. The brain changes the side of dominant activity roughly every ninety minutes. This is why, when traveling a familiar route, either you can't remember driving through a familiar village—or you notice an old cottage that you had not remembered seeing before. When the right brain is dominant you only see the big picture because you are on autopilot. When the left brain takes over, you notice every detail in your immediate environment.

This problem shows up in developmental delays. Children with dyspraxia are also fearful of change. When anyone enters a new situation, the right side of the brain accesses the new situation to determine if it is safe. It is the approach and withdrawal center that checks first and foremost for the individual's safely.

We are familiar with this process. When we enter a new dentist's office, we first take a look around the room. Then we take a seat. After a few moments pass, when our left brain has taken over, we look around and notice details. However, this does not happen until the right brain has decided that all is safe. A child with a developmental delay has a right brain that finds it difficult to relax and feel safe, and a left brain that is under-functioning.

OCD

Obsessive compulsive disorder is a marked by a compulsion to perform certain acts repetitively and to carry out certain rituals. These can dominate the child's life, where exacting order and routines are very difficult to maintain.

This problem also manifests in adults, who spend hours each day performing exacting compulsions that affect them both mentally and physically. For example, sufferers may wash their hands repeatedly until the skin becomes raw and chapped. Or the items in their desks must be arranged in exacting orders.

An obsession is an idea, thought, impulse or a mental image that seems rational. The person understands that the thought is coming from himself. However, because of an unreasonable inner compulsion, the individual acts out the thought again and again until it becomes obsessive.

An example of this is the way an individual who struggles with OCD will handle turning a light off. First he flips the switch. He sees that the light has been turned off as the room darkens. Yet as he walks away, the thought begins to nag him that perhaps he did not actually turn the light off. What if it is still on? So he finally returns to the room to verify that the light was turned off. Yet after he leaves the room, the nagging question continues to prod him. What if he imagined checking to see that the light was off? He may check repeatedly to be sure the light is off until the obsession is satisfied.

He has acted on his compulsion in an effort to reduce anxiety or fear. A compulsion to check whether a candle was blown out can reduce the fear of the house being burned down. The physical action helps satisfy the discomfort of having to fight the nagging thoughts away.

In order to have a secure environment, people with OCD try to place objects in exactly the right position, touch or smell objects repeatedly, and feel driven to be perfect. They are hyper-vigilant, and they avoid situations where they cannot control the environment. OCD is more than just perfectionism, because it disrupts daily normal routine functions due to thought patterns that are driving the individual.

People with OCD know that what they are doing is irrational, but feel that they cannot control their thoughts and behaviors. Their lives are filled with worry and avoiding troublesome situations. They find it very difficult to live, and they depend on other people for their reassurance.

People with OCD repeat tasks because they feel they did not do the job competently the first time. Sometimes they fear superstitions, and feel obsessive obligations to do things a specific number of times. They have certain rituals they feel they must perform in a certain order, as when they are brushing their teeth or preparing to go away. Experiencing OCD can make normal routines difficult to handle. Examples of this are found in sorting laundry, handling oneself in a restaurant or using public restrooms. The individual may also develop a self-destructive habit, such as biting the lips until they are sore and chapped.

Interventions for OCD

- When a person with OCD is obsessing in a ritual, guide him to a proactive choice. Tell him, "Stop. Get focused. Are you ready to start now?" Coach him through the next steps.

- Set limits for the amount of time the individual can spend on an activity.

- Don't try to stop all the OCD rituals at once. Target the most disruptive ones.

- When the individual is stuck on a compulsion, try to distract him with something else.

Tourette's Syndrome

Tourette's Syndrome is a rare form of generalized tic. It usually begins when the individual is between two and fifteen years of age. Some tics are uncontrolled continuous gestures such as repeating what others say, facial twitching or foul language.

Tics are sudden involuntary movements that occur repeatedly. There are various kinds of tics including eye-blinking, clearing the throat, sniffing, barking, arm flapping, word repeating or shoulder jerking. These can happen at any time. While most people find that they have some brief control over their tics, keeping the urges suppressed may create aggravated outbreaks later. Being anxious or fatigued can also increase the action of tics. Sleeping or doing something absorbing may reduce the problem. However, while something like electronic games may reduce tics, the individual may also have increased irritability later.

While most children who suffer with Tourette's have average intelligence, they tend to have trouble transitioning mentally from one topic to another. They find it difficult to take new ideas and connect them to other relevant information in a creative way. Some of these individuals have food allergies, and need to avoid sugar and caffeine. They may also be sensitive to perfumes and other smells.

Interventions for Tourette's Syndrome

Students with Tourette's tend to have trouble communicating because of the tics getting in the way. They often stutter. Give them the amount of time they need to answer for themselves. And do not allow other students to answer for them.

Tics do create problems. At test time, a tic can be annoying. Allow the student to go to the office or out into the hallway. Since children often imitate the responses of the teacher, the teacher can help by maintaining a calm attitude that diffuses tension in the classroom. Be compassionate, and require that your other students show respect and understanding.

Some tics are embarrassing. It may be possible to guide a certain tic into another more appropriate tic. For example, if the tic is spitting at or licking others, perhaps the individual can help redirect the urge to become a swallowing tic, or licking his own teeth. Redirecting tics becomes easier as people get older. Help them to pardon themselves if they are not able to control an inappropriate tic.

Because stress aggravates tics, it is important to help students organize their days into a schedule. Inform them in advance of any unusual happening for the day. Because of the anticipation and nervousness they can produce, anticipated events such as field trips and school programs often increase the frequency with which the child will need to deal with his tic. Listening to soft music on the way to an event can be calming.

Advise students in advance if there will be visitors. Give them time-frames in which to expect the next change of events. So as the school day closes, you may announce, "We will be getting ready to go home in thirty minutes."

Autism
Autistic children are like lost children, wandering in their own worlds. There is diversity under the autistic umbrella, ranging from those who have minor issues to those who require full-time care.

Autism involves impaired social skills, in which the child has trouble initiating connections or responding to those coming from others. The autistic child has trouble focusing on people, and knowing when it is appropriate to smile. When their names are called, they may not respond. Though they do not appear to be listening, they sometimes know everything that has been said.

These children have difficulty expressing their needs and desires, and expect others to know what they are thinking or wanting. The world they live in is a small one with no connections to others. Basically only aware of themselves, they do not try to connect, or even desire those connections. This creates a problem in being included by their peers. And building friendships is almost impossible.

Autistic children make motions repetitively. A child may spin the tires on his toy car or wave his hand as if it were an airplane wing for extended periods of time. While they do this, they are not aware of what is going on around them. Sometimes they will pick up words they hear, and echo them repeatedly.

These children are often hypersensitive to sensory input. Background noises that the average person ignores sound louder and can actually produce pain. Being in crowds can drive the autistic child to distraction. It is important that the caregiver recognizes stressor signals. Covering his ears with his hands, squeezing his eyes shut, becoming loud or angry, refusing to move, becoming irrational or shutting down emotionally can all be signs of overload. The child will also find it difficult to make eye contact.

While a child with autism is usually characterized by difficulty interacting well with other people, a child whose autism has been further defined as Asperger's Syndrome tends to be a bit more socially oriented. He usually has at least average intelligence, and an obsessive orientation. Aspergers's children do not deal with a language developmental disorder.

Children with Asperger's may grimace or have an odd running gait, facial tics or poor motor control. When they are excited, they may lapse into rocking, or may flap their hands.

Children with Asperger's, as we have noted, are on the high-functioning edge of the autistic spectrum. They are usually intelligent, yet relate to others in strange ways. They are not good listeners or empathizers. Because they cannot read and respond to other people's feelings and emotions well, they often appear to be uncaring.

The child with Asperger's would often rather read about facts than fiction, because he has difficulty thinking with imagination. His logic runs in literal lines, leaving him unaffected by peer pressure.

These children find it hard to interact with others and have difficulty looking into another person's eyes. Sometimes their conversations are one-sided. Following an expected routine increases their level of security, as well as following rituals. When they become disturbed, they have meltdowns. Caregivers must be prepared to share volumes of redirection and reassurance.

Interventions for Autistic Children
· Autistic children's problems center around their lack of social skills and unawareness of those around them. Teaching appropriate social behavior is highly important.

· As you teach a child emotional awareness, the use of pictures is important.

· Give the child a reference point. As you are working with the child, say, "Look at Jonathan running around the circle. Now it's your turn. Can you do that?"

· Encourage making requests. Just give the child a small amount of snack. Wait to give him more until he asks for it.

· Help the child make choices. Present two options and ask, "Which one do you want?"

- Use your example to encourage imitation. Get your student's attention by saying, "Look. Watch what I am doing." Use the same routine every time. Or say, "Do what I do. Now you do it, John." Praise the child for accomplishments. If he is not able to do a task, gently help him complete the action, with decreasing help, until he can do it successfully on his own.

- Use touch and praise. When others touch us, it breaks the field we generally call personal space. Many autistic children majorly live in their own space. When you praise them, giving them a small squeeze or a pat on the shoulder helps you enter their personal space, reinforcing the praise. Make sure you have parental permission to touch the child.

- Always be aware of sensory avoidance. If the child is pulling away, he may be communicating that touch does not feel good to him. Other appropriate rewards can also be used —verbal praise, small bits of food, high fives, stickers, pennies, puzzle pieces and so on. Use these as incentives rather than bribery.

- Integrate the child into life. Be aware of his sensory overloads, but don't dismiss him from meeting any responsibilities. For instance, have the child sit with others (perhaps on the perimeters). Be careful not to excuse the child from an activity on the pretext of sensory overload when he could simply be in a stubborn streak.

- Help the child find refreshment by hugging a ball for a few minutes, taking a short walk or giving comfort hugs.

Things to Keep in Mind
- Plan wisely as a parent or teacher. Transition from one activity to another. The child's awkward running gait will hinder some games. Spatial orientation problems contribute to their confusion. Handwriting may be a problem if hypersensitivity

causes the pencil hold to become painful. Avoid placing these children beside windows, hallways and so on.

- Be literal. Say exactly what you mean without using idioms. If you use them, the student may not understand what you are saying because his mind is using a very literal approach. Most of our communication is nonverbal, and autistic children miss a lot of these social cues.

- Watch for bolting. This should be a concern for teachers and parents. Have a plan, whether or not the child has bolted before, since bolting becomes a safety issue for the child. Have lists of instructions ready so that you will be prepared if an emergency occurs. This would include phone numbers for caregivers, and medical information in the event that an injury should occur. Create a list of people who could help in an emergency. This list could include teachers, older students and etc.

- Some children love the thrill of being chased. It is important that the child learns the meaning of "Stop!" Bolting can sometimes be stopped by rhythm patterns such as patting the child's leg, or having him bounce a ball.

- Be prepared for tantrums. When one occurs, reduce your language. When the child is in a full-blown tantrum, say firmly, "Stop! Sit down on your chair." Think about any triggers that could have affected the child. What may have triggered the child to feel out of control? What was not clear to him?

※ ※ ※

A lot of learning disabilities are hard to pick up on. The children we are working with appear to be so normal; they have no visible handicaps that set them apart. They are not wearing hearing aids, braces or prostheses. As a result, these children are often misunderstood. And teachers and parents come to the conclusion that the children are being lazy, not listening, acting stubborn—or just being careless.

Their intelligence can be very near average—or even above that. And some days they can perform well. However, the next day may be a different story.

It is assumed that the child can hear. But does he? It is believed that he has good vision. Yet sometimes it appears he cannot see what is in front of his eyes. These children experience difficulty in learning that is not caused by inadequate education or cultural factors.

Difficulty in learning is produced because the child has poor perception or cannot conceptualize. Other children have problems processing or using language, or have lack of motor control. Memory and attention skills are also deficient.

The child experiences a loss in his sense of worth because he does not understand his own problems. Other people accomplish tasks he cannot do. And he wonders why he is so dumb, when he works harder and longer than his peers—and still cannot perform.

These children find problems at two levels. First of all they need to decide what the speaker means. The next task is determining what they are expected to do. Generally a child is not being stubborn or careless, or failing to pay attention. Rather, connections that need to be made in the wiring of his brain are not being processed. Therefore he suffers in not being able to perform as expected.

The following lists will help you identify various learning disabilities.

Visual Perception

This is often associated with dyslexia. The eye doctor may say that the child has 20/20 vision, and there may not be any problem with the way the eye is functioning. Yet there is a problem because the brain is not processing information properly and is therefore not correctly interpreting what the eyes are seeing. Look for the following:

- Letter reversals *(b & d, p & q)*.

- Inversions *(u & n, w & m)*.

- Yawning frequently when reading.

- Complaining that his eyes hurt, or rubbing his eyes while reading.

- Finding that print is blurry; not seeing well.

- Holding the head at odd angles. These children don't complain about double vision, because it is the way they have always experienced sight. Jason covered one eye. Jean always saw two of everything, but thought other people did too.

- Closing one eye while working.

- Not copying words and facts accurately.

- Losing his place while reading.

- Rereading lines, skipping lines, or needing to use a marker.

- Needing larger print, or a marker with a slit.

- Having trouble with sequencing properly (as in was/saw, God/dog, on/no).

- Being slow to pick up likenesses and differences.

- Doing a lot of erasing.

- Having trouble discerning depth perception (as in failing to meet the ball with the bat, clumsily running into things, or knocking things off counters).

Visual Perceptual/Visual Motor Deficits

· Letters colliding with each other.

· Letters not on lines.

· Letters formed in odd ways.

· Mirror writing.

· Inability to color within lines.

· Illegible writing.

· Pencil held too tightly.

· Inability to cut on lines.

· Trouble pasting.

· Messy papers.

Spatial Relationships/Body Awareness Deficits

· Experiencing directional problems, as in reading backwards, copying words and shapes backward or upside down.

· Getting lost in familiar surroundings.

· Having problems

· Keeping columns straight in math.

· Bumping into things; being clumsy or accident-prone.

· Having difficulty understanding concepts such as over/under, around/through, first/last, front/back, and so on.

· Having trouble keeping eyes closed; getting dizzy and falling off a stool or out of a desk; falling easily at recess.

Auditory Perceptual Deficits

- Not "getting" conversation, with a lost, confused look on his face.

- Not hearing the difference in the sounds of b, d & p; n & m; g & j; not always hearing final consonants accurately.

- Not being able to tell which direction sounds come from.

- Having difficulty understanding what he hears. (Auditory training programs help with this issue.)

- Not being able to filter out extra noises, or having trouble distinguishing a parent's or teacher's voice from others; perceiving an incorrect answer.

- Not following directions.

- Not benefiting from oral instruction.

Conceptual Difficulties

- Not reading body language.

- Not seeing relationships between similar ideas.

- Not being able to compare how things are alike/different; having difficulty classifying items.

- Not understanding time relationships such as today/tomorrow, and before/after.

- Not associating an act with its logical outcome.

- Having little imagination.

- Not "getting" a joke.

- Lacking expression.

- Being slow to respond.

- Having difficulty coming up with creative ideas for composition, or in forming a story after he has seen a picture.

- Having trouble projecting what to do next, or what the next picture is in a picture sequence.

- Not thinking in an orderly fashion.

- Not understanding emotions.

- Making classroom comments that are abstract or bizarre.

- Frequently mispronouncing common words.

Memory Deficits

- Not remembering what he just saw.

- Not remembering what he just heard.

- Not being able to repeat a four-number sequence.

- Having trouble copying math facts.

- Having difficulty remembering familiar spellings.

- Remembering things of long ago better than recent events.

- Finding it hard to memorize; making lots of mistakes.

- Appearing to know something one day, but having no reference to it the next.

- Limiting expressive language, as in talking about "that thing."

- Limiting receptive language, as in not understanding what is said, or not connecting to others' thoughts.

- Making the same error over and over.

- Having poor writing habits; not remembering to capitalize, punctuate or indent.

Motor Output Difficulty

- Giving the same response repeatedly.

- Not being able to hop, skip or jump very far; having trouble hitting and kicking balls, jumping rope, and so on.

- Having difficulty cutting, pasting, coloring and writing.

- Being able to point to a correct spelling, but not copying it correctly.

- Being able to dictate a story or sentence, but having trouble writing it.

- Making lots of disturbing noises.

- Having odd tics and funny movements.

Attention Deficit Disorder

- Tending to have a stomachache in the morning.

- Having good days and bad days, as opposed to being stable.

- Being the classroom clown because he would rather be thought of as funny than dumb.

- Not sitting still; having poor posture; wrapping feet and legs around chair legs, and so on.

- Not being able to stand still.

- Not being able to keep his eyes closed.

- Being impulsive; not considering what might happen before he does something.

- Having a low frustration tolerance level.

- Finding it hard to finish assignments within given time frames.

- Being visually distracted, and looking up to see all visual stimuli.

- Being distracted by what he hears, and feeling the need to look toward the source of every noise.

- Being very fidgety, drumming fingers, tapping toes, rolling pencils; always playing with something; making mouth noises and talking all the time.

- Having a very short attention span.

- Being a daydreamer who produces little work.

- "Spacing out" when he feels overwhelmed, especially when something new is being taught.

- Being very negative; feeling that everything is wrong and that no one likes him.

- Not minding his own affairs.

- Tending to be a bully.

- Not following rules.

- Having mood swings.

- Being very disorganized; losing papers, books, lunch boxes, coats, and so on.

- Responding poorly to correction; projecting an "I'm so dumb" image.

Emotional Problems
- Being explosive and unpredictable.

- Lacking enthusiasm for anything.

- Telling bizarre stories; seeming to be confused between reality and fantasy.

- Not feeling for others.

- Withdrawing from others; being a loner; not communicating well.

- Feeling that others "pick on" him.

- Not assuming responsibility.

- Being fearful, anxious and insecure.

chapter ten

Priorities for the Severely Limited Child

Working with severely limited children requires a very mature sense of understanding. We must know the abilities the child does or does not have. We will not be able to teach him everything we desire to, and sometimes the gains will seem minimal. Yet the efforts are worthwhile. Every small increment gained is another step in the path to healing for the child, and an improvement in the lives of both himself and his family.

It is critical to understand that the child has a very short attention span. Some of these children cannot look at something for more than thirty seconds—or two minutes at the most. Change activities often. However, do not let the child rule the schedule with his complaints. If he begs to quit, is tired or cries, encourage him to do one or two more of whatever you are doing. That way you are in charge.

While this very short attention span many not seem reasonable to you, it is very real in terms of the child's ability to cope. So it is not wise to keep on and on with an activity he can barely do. To do so would be damaging.

These children have a limited capacity. When you try an activity that you thought the child could do, and it is not working—back off. Take smaller steps, and see if you can arrive at that spot later.

You will know that you are pushing the child beyond his limits if he cries easily and a personality that is usually sweet turns sour. Parents also provide a good thermometer on the child's tolerances if they tell the teacher that the child cannot cope at home—or vice versa. If the child loses bathroom control, becomes unworkable or begins hurting other children, consider that a line may have been crossed.

Most of these children have physical limitations. Make sure that you know what those are. A knowledgeable doctor is a great asset. Parents can share with the child's teacher the information they have learned about their child's handicap, as well as their own experiences.

Are there any activities that become a safety issue for the child? Is he allergic to anything? What foods should be avoided? Some handicapped children have heart issues. Joint issues are another common malady.

Are there any structural problems or positions that could potentially cause injury? For example, some Down's children have a neck weakness and should not try to do somersaults. Also be aware of any blood conditions that would make bumps and bruises dangerous. Some children also bruise more easily than others.

If you are a teacher doing therapy with the child, make sure that you watch the parents or therapist working with the child at regular intervals. And if you have new ideas that you believe will be helpful, share your information with the parents and therapist, and ask permission before you begin. Not all therapies are for every child.

I have found that introducing too much at a time confuses our very limited children. They will never learn by leaps and bounds. Be content with slow progress that keeps going forward as far as the child can progress. A mind stretched by a new idea will never return to the same dimension. So go ahead and stretch by small increments, knowing that stretching too hard will cause unnecessary stress and frustration—for everyone.

Teachers should avoid teaching a new concept in every class in one day. I generally found that one or two new ideas in a school day was about the limit for my severely limited students.

Sometimes I found it worked best to introduce a new idea one day without incorporating the concept into the child's work. One or two days later, I could come back to the new material and give the student an assignment using the concept.

I had a student who would freeze or lock up every time he heard the word "new." It was impossible for Jeremy to do well on any new concept just learned that day. I began using the board to show the whole class "something fun," presenting the new material I wanted to introduce to Jeremy. As I worked with the new concept with Jeremy the next day, I would say, "This is what I showed you yesterday, remember?" And Jeremy could easily do his lesson.

Stay focused on the child's emotional flexibility. If the child is being pressured, you will see the sparkle leave his eyes. Or he may give you a blank, spaced-out look.

Since most of these children cannot pick up verbal cues and body language, be sure to tell them what is about to happen in advance. In a very emotionally brittle child, a temper tantrum is often a reaction to something he does not understand—by which he feels threatened.

Rochelle was two when I began working with her. Every morning she had a temper tantrum while her mother dressed her. We wondered why, and realized that when her mother carried her downstairs, she would say, "Come! We're going downstairs to eat breakfast." However, Rochelle's mother carried her past the set table in the dining room as she walked to the changing table to dress the little girl. Did Rochelle assume that there would be no breakfast for her? So we did an experiment. When her mother brought her downstairs, she explained that she would first dress Rochelle, and then they would go to the table. With that explanation, Rochelle nicely allowed her mother to dress her.

We all desire to impact life around us and to control some things about our lives. The severely limited child is no exception. Since other people will need to make many choices for him, try to find something that will give him the option of making a choice every day.

This becomes a part of building a healthy sense of personhood—of knowing that he matters. Every person longs to share his voice and be heard, to enjoy mutual relationships that make the heart grow, to impact others and to have some sense of control about his own life. Personhood is a gift that God has given to each man or woman. We follow God's directives when we help build these qualities into the children we touch.

chapter eleven

Working With Special Needs

Whether they belong to us biologically or by adoption, all children are precious stewardships loaned to us from God. God has created each soul, and He delights to light His lamp within each one. He wants to bless us and lead us in the paths of righteousness—and to bring Himself glory.

What is good parenting from a brain-based perspective? How can we nourish the life God has given to each child, to bring it into full bloom as God intended?

It is important that a parent be sensitive and emotionally responsive to his child's desire for legitimate attention. Children should know that they are "seen," that they matter, and that they are valued. It is not enough to feed and clothe a child, for he has a spirit and soul that will live forever. In Chapter Three, we shared the importance of giving our children the total message that we see who they are as persons, and that we are delighted to be with them.

Nancy was thirty when I learned to know her. She suffered from depression, lack of motivation and inner deadness. While her parents were not evil people, the warpedness of their own hearts had overwhelmed them. Instead of finding answers for themselves, they had continued to fumble through life—and Nancy had grown up believing that she did not matter. She thought that no one would approve of her since she was so slow and unorganized. She was unworthy. In the face of these lies, her sense of hope had shriveled and died.

Nancy and I talked about many things. Some of those were the lies she had come to believe about herself. She found it hard to fathom that anyone would want to know her—and value the person they met. That she could make personal choices. And that she should seek for the love Christ was offering to her. "Edith," she asked in amazement, "Do you mean that it's all right to ask for love?"

One of the ways we teach children the tender love of God is the way we comfort them when they are injured or stressed out. As you hold a troubled child in your arms, you provide a safe shelter that assures them that things will be all right again. That they have a safe place to go when life becomes troublesome. And that they can return to joy after sorrow. This is the basis on which a child's security is built.

Helping a child return to joy after he is disappointed is his mother's job for the first two years of his life. When we teach this to our children, we are teaching them a skill they will carry with them for life. Otherwise, we can expect to see these individuals become teenagers and adults who will tend to pity themselves instead of facing life wholesomely.

Susan was ten when I began working with her neurological issues. "I think I must be retarded," she said. I assured her that she was a normal human being. And as she improved on the program, she was amazed at the positive changes that came into her life. She could finally catch a ball! Reading was becoming easier. And as she was able to contribute to relationships with more confidence, the number of her friends increased. "Joan," she said, as her eyes sparkled into mine, "thank you for telling me I wasn't retarded."

Words, wisely and carefully chosen, have tremendous power to give life and bless people. Speak healing words into the hearts of your children. Share words that wrap comfort around a small, quaking child—like a soft blanket. Encouraging words put courage and purpose into the souls of small people who must learn to live in a sin-cursed world. We need to assure them that we are walking beside them, that we know the way, and that we will help them. They can count on us!

Another important task to accomplish with your child is to teach him the joy of mutual friendships. As a parent, you have the wonderful opportunity to shape your child's heart for meaningful relationships— by being a good first companion when your child is learning how to enjoy staying connected with others. If your child learns that it is safe to be close with another person, his heart will be open to live and grow. Otherwise, he will shut love out of his life—because he will fear being hurt in closeness.

We also need wisdom to know when it is time to let our children struggle and work through challenges to build their own resilience. We must know when to offer some help, and then watch as they battle on their own. As the child becomes able to meet his own challenges, there is a time and place where we need to step back to give him the opportunity to develop his own resources.

It is the same lesson we learn from a butterfly. We have watched butterflies struggle intensely as they break out of their chrysalises, looking wet, weary and bedraggled. But then we have also shared the pure delight as the gilded wings take to the air and drift away beyond our sight. And we know that without the struggle, the butterfly's wings would never have developed to the point of usefulness.

Ways to Help Toddlers Develop Proper Neurological Pathways

We have discussed the need for eye contact with our babies. The same remains true as a child moves into the toddler stage. Your child will need this kind of nurture for the remainder of his life.

Physical touch remains important. Our little ones need to feel our gentle touches, and sometimes the reassurance of a strong hand grasp. Rub your child's head and play with his ears. The ears contain multitudes of sensors that affect various areas. At the toddler stage you will not carry him most of the time. Instead, hold his little hand with pleasure.

A toddler begins to experience swings, sliding boards, and tunnels to crawl through. If you allow your toddler to use a trampoline, make sure that he is on the trampoline by himself, and that you have a safety net around the perimeter. A lot of neck and back injuries have occurred when trampolines were used carelessly.

Have fun together, or invent games, where you teach your toddler to hop like a bunny, skip and jump. Let a child twirl as much as he wants to. That is how balance is developed. Play ball, pitching and catching, or roll a ball back and forth. Use two balls—and then three balls to challenge the child.

Encourage activities that use hand-over-hand activities. Pull up a chair to the kitchen counter and let the child help you stir cookie dough. Make a game out of folding washcloths. You are also teaching the child to contribute to the family and to be a part of a "we" group as he does so. This will develop a sense of being a worthwhile person who has something to give others, and the joy of giving selflessly.

Signals That Spell T-R-O-U-B-L-E

- Tactile defense—We see this when a child flinches and startles after he is two months old. If the retained reflexes that cause this are not integrated (or retired), the child/adult will find it hard to express his emotions, and will live in a fight-or-flight mode—always running from the "tiger," as the expression goes.

- Poor clinging or holding on when you carry the child—because the child does not have a proper sense of danger.

- Resistance to cuddling; stiffness—The child who resists cuddling may be stuck in the fight-or-flight mode, where he is on an overly alert status. In that case, the child feels too vulnerable to accept cuddling.

- Poor eye contact—If the child's eyes are not tracking well and working together efficiently, he will have multitudes of issues to deal with, and many things that he will fear. Vision issues create insecurity in a child, who may also lack coordination.

- Unreasonable irritability—Children act the way they feel. When they remain irritable, there is usually something wrong. The child could be feeling lots of mental confusion on a regular basis.

- Randall came to see me when he was four. His parents questioned his level of intelligence because Randall did not respond to commands or make small talk. As I tested him, I discovered that his auditory skills were poor. In fact, it almost appeared that he could not hear. When I stood directly in front of him and talked directly to him, he did respond. I had his parents take a PVC pipe phone and talk gently into one of his ears, and Randall began to respond appropriately. When he failed to understand what was being spoken to him, Randal would go for his PVC pipe phone. Randall had not been able to process the signals his ears were transmitting to his brain for interpretation. An auditory training unit aided him.

- Hyperactivity—This describes the child who cannot hold still because his brain requires constant stimulation. This also includes the children who fall off the chairs they are sitting on, and who find it hard to close their eyes when they pray, because they lose the sense of where they are when their eyes are shut.

- Crying easily, and being fragile emotionally—Does your child cry on very little pretext? Is he overwhelmed and frustrated with small changes in life? Does he present with temper tantrums when change is taking place? When a child's brain is in overload, it takes very little until he is overwhelmed and in tears.

- Not getting along with peers—Something is wrong if your child prefers playing by himself most of the time. These children find it much less confusing to fit into their own plans than to figure out what others are trying to do and how to fit into their plans. It is much easier for a child to carry out his own agendas than it is to figure out how to carry out another's.

- Inability to comprehend verbal messages—If you need to hold your child's chin in your hand and look into his eyes for him to process what you are saying, there is a problem. It would appear that the child is not comprehending speech without making eye contact, and that making eye contact is difficult for him.

- Walking without coordination—This is the clumsy child who falls, runs into things, and accidentally breaks things. In a case like this, we could be looking at poor visual skills as well as lack of coordination.

- Eyestrain—If your child often has headaches, has itchy or tired eyes, or covers one eye with his hand, look for problems. When we have poor eye teaming, the eyes are working much harder to function than they should. This creates eyestrain.

· Frequent carsickness—This usually means we are dealing with balance issues.

· An eye that is lazy—When this occurs, we are seeing poor eye teaming, poor balance, and a head righting reflex that needs correction.

· Difficulty sleeping—If your child doesn't sleep well, has racing brain patterns, or is hard to settle, something is probably going on at the neurological level. Benadryl can be used for short-term sleeping problems, or for the odd time when this is a problem.

· Difficulty with mounting steps—If going up and down stairs is a problem, consider that your child may have a vision problem.

· Problems with memorizing—If your child cannot memorize well, try developing his auditory system with a PVC pipe telephone. (See directions for this in the appendix at the back of the book.) Auditory training units, which are more effective than the PVC pipe phones, can also be purchased for use at home.

· Difficulty with unreasonable temper tantrums—A child who is not able to deal with transition may be suffering because he did not receive his protein snack. It often helps if these children are given plenty of advance notice that something different will be done.

· Wetting the bed—Children wet the bed for various reasons. Their bladders may be too small. They may be sleeping too deeply. Sometimes bedwetting is a sign that the child is being abused. If the problem is a bladder weakness, we use exercises to correct the problem.

Are there reasons for these behaviors?

As the brain develops, both sides should learn to work equally well. We do not want to see children developing brain dominance until they are about one and a half to two and a half years old. When a client tells me that her baby has already established a dominant side, I know that we are in trouble. A baby should use either hand equally well, and each foot should be kicking with equal skill.

As healthy dominance develops, one hemisphere of the brain steps out as the leader, and the other follows. Sometimes this break is never made. At other times the break has happened—but the gap between the two sides is too large, and one side is doing too much of the work.

Either one of these reasons can cause the child to give up easily because his brain is overwhelmed. Or he may become angry without reasonable cause, because he lives in constant frustration. Transition and change seem intolerable to the child, and he throws fits as he shuts down.

When both sides of the brain fight for dominance, we have a brain experiencing civil war. In that case the child remains locked in what people often call "the terrible twos." Adults who respond in the same way children do, thinking only of themselves, may be neurologically stuck at this level.

In situations where dominance has been established in the brain, and the gap is too big between the two hemispheres of the brain, one side is much too active while the other side is asleep. Children with this symptom respond in various ways. They may be very passive and need lots of sleep. They also have limited resources and tend to give up easily. These are the children who say, "I can't," "I don't know how," or "Help me!" over and over.

What can we do to prevent these behaviors?

We must give our babies tummy time, tummy time, and more

tummy time! So much good development takes place while the child is exercising the muscles he uses when he plays on his stomach. In addition to speech, chewing, visual, and good core muscle control issues that are developed while the child plays on his tummy, he will be better prepared to crawl correctly when that stage of neurological development comes. Good eye and brain function depend on four or five months of crawling correctly.

Eating often enough is very important to little folks. Since a baby's stomach is small, he needs to be fed at least every two to three hours. A good protein snack will sometimes help with persistent temper tantrums.

Seeing that your child has an optimum amount of sleep does wonders. We find that a large percentage of learning disabilities stems from lack of sleep. While the child sleeps, the brain grows and refreshes itself. An infant needs fourteen to eighteen hours of sleep within a twenty-four hour period. Toddlers should have twelve to fifteen hours. For growing children, figure no less than ten to twelve hours per night.

Invest in time spent with your child that will encourage trust and companionship to grow. Bonding with parents is so essential to a child's well-being that one researcher has suggested that most of the hyperactivity and learning disabilities we see today go back to a lack of the mother bond in the child. Talk. Share. See into the heart of your child. Bless the budding life.

One approach that diminishes stress in challenged children is preparing them well in advance for changes in schedules and activities. When we help them to feel comfortable with transition when their coping resources are small, they feel less overwhelmed and threatened by the changes.

It may be necessary to retell the child his life story to help him understand why he has certain fears and why he responds the way he does in certain situations. Talk freely with your child about his past. Explain to the child that it is not his fault that things happened the way they did, but that he is suffering because of sin other people committed. And reassure him that you will help him to learn to handle life in a wholesome way. God created us as people who can make choices.

Begin to explain the path of forgiveness to your child. In a simple way, share your own trust in God, and the rest you find in depending on Him. Assure your child that Jesus tenderly loves little children, and that God will always be with us. Add that in heaven, everything will be joyful!

Be firmly in control of your child's life and behavior. If we are not wise enough or strong enough to control them, our children innately know that we are not strong enough to provide for their safety.

Checkpoints for Challenged Children

· Have the child's eyesight checked by a doctor. Simple eye tests can also be done at school. I have had several little girls who were doing poorly. After their eyes were checked, we knew the reason. Each of them had one eye that was nearly blind.

· Have the child's hearing checked, including auditory processing. Use a PVC pipe phone if there is a problem. Daryl was an eight-year-old boy who had trouble connecting with his parents. He was also difficult to handle. When I asked his parents what kind of gifting meant the most to him, they suggested that it might be physical touch. I suggested that they lay a hand on his shoulder when they talked to him, or offer him "good night" hugs. His parents did, and Daryl responded warmly. Immediately it became easier to connect with the boy. There were still other issues to keep resolving, but having a smoother relationship made those easier.

· Make sure the child is getting adequate sleep.

- Make sure your child is getting a good diet with wholesome body and brain-building foods.

- If the child cannot handle a task, consider the reason. You can often break a larger task into smaller ones that are manageable.

- Find out what type of gifting reaches the child's heart to build him up. It means so much to know that someone truly cares for us.

Helping Your Child Deal with Fears

Children are afraid of many things. There is the fear of falling. Many children share a fear of the dark. When I was five, I was afraid that when I returned from Sunday School, all the mothers would look alike, and I would not know which one belonged to me.

Are these fears reasonable? Sometimes fears have a valid base. If we step too close to the edge of a precipice, we may fall. In that case, fear protects us by alerting us to take danger seriously. In the case of my fear that I would not be able to find my mother because all the women would look alike, the concern was not substantiated. Some fears are realistic and some are not. Yet to the persons experiencing them, they produce real problems that need to be handled.

As you share with your child, empathize with him without reinforcing the fears he has. When he tells you that he is afraid of the dark, tell him that you used to fear the darkness too. Acknowledging your child's fears will help him work through them. Discuss the fear issue without blowing it up to crisis stage. When he tells you after dark in the evening that he left his bike out in the yard and that he is afraid of bears, offer to go along with him. While you are there, sit on the edge of the porch for a few minutes and look at the stars.

Childhood is full of scary first-time encounters. As you teach him the way through fear, you will teach him coping patterns that will be there to help him for the remainder of his life.

When a child has faced his fears and stepped out to do something with shaking knees and a pounding heart—that is something worth acknowledging and celebrating! Take a moment to affirm your child's bravery with words of affirmation. "You make me so happy! I saw that you were afraid, but you did it anyway. You were very brave and courageous." It is crucial that we build our children's confidence, especially in the area of things they fear.

Some of the things children fear include moving to another home or community, taking one's first trip to the dentist, dealing with animals, sleeping alone in a dark room, or going to visit a new church.

Play the "What If?" game with your child. By uncovering our fears and determining a safe path we could take through a situation, the power of fear becomes diffused, and we are able to establish a sense of control. What if you are at school, and you throw up? What if you are at a sleep-over and someone tells a scary story? What if no one picks you for the ball game? And what if Grandma serves peaches—which you don't like? Discussing problems and finding a way through, brings problems back to a level that we can usually manage.

Life is filled with both large and small disappointments. Your child will not always be invited to the party, and he may fail a test. The best training ground for dealing with disappointing situations is a loving home with parents who will respond with kindness and teach their children to learn from their mistakes. Maintaining God-fearing attitudes helps us to look at things in a wholesome way. When our children fall, we help them dust themselves off and go on to try harder the next time.

Although our words communicate grand visions, they also communicate our displeasure. Words have the power to build up a life—or destroy it. We can use words unwisely and shatter the dreams of children. Or we can spark flames of passion with a few aptly-chosen words.

The pain of loneliness is sharp, destroying hope when it is needed the most. We all long to be loved, accepted and affirmed by our community. Our children feel this even more strongly than a mature individual. Is your child afraid that he will not be able to fit into his new classroom when a new school year starts? Or have you moved into a new community? Watch your child for signs that he needs help to process change, or with fitting in and making new friends.

We are all very sensitive about the way our peers rate our appearance. As children struggle to find their places within their small social groups, their internal radar zooms in on anything that is slightly abnormal. Then children's words become weapons. "Move over, Fatty!" "Hey, four-eyes!" "String Bean, throw that ball to me." Those words hang in the air for a fraction of a second until they are absorbed in the heart of the listener. Shame and embarrassment set in. Lies are believed in the soul of the child. Most children find it easier to laugh than to retaliate with words or fists. But often the tears come later.

Consider Mary's story.
I grew up knowing that I was different, and I hated it. I was born with a cleft palate. When I went to school, my classmates jeered and mocked me. "What happened to your lip, Mary? Did the buzzards eat it?" and "Why do you talk like a baby?" Then they would run off laughing, thinking that they had cracked brilliant jokes. And my heart smarted.

I would tell the children that I had fallen and cut my mouth on a piece of glass. Somehow it seemed more acceptable to have suffered an accident than to have been born different. I was convinced that no one outside my family could love me.

There was, however, a teacher in the second grade whom we all adored, Mrs. Leonard by name. She was short, round, happy and sparkling. Our school had an annual hearing test. I remembered from first grade that we would stand against the door, cover one ear and see if we could repeat the words our teacher whispered. Sometimes the words were, "The sky is blue," or "Do you have new shoes?" When it was my turn, I waited to hear what she would say. What she said were eight words that would change my life. My heart throbbed with joy when I heard her whisper, "Mary, I wish you were my little girl."

❧ ❧ ❧

There are ways in which most challenged children can contribute to others, and find that the world is larger than themselves. A Down's child can be taught to be polite and courteous. Find roles your children can fill to contribute to family projects that are for the good of everyone. Teach them to make cards, or to pray for others. Most challenged children can be taught not to whine, and to respect others. They can learn to wait patiently until it is their turn for attention.

Regardless of the way they feel, our goal is to teach children the beginning steps to responding to the world we are in—with good choices. Building our thoughts on the truth of God's Word, shaping our attitudes as humble servants who want to please their Master, and acting in obedience to God's will for our lives are the keys to translating God's gifts and directives into living faith. We teach those concepts in two ways: by modeling them for our children, and by teaching them the beginning steps to living by the standard of truth in the fear of God.

Our goal is to teach every child to be a competent, whole person who knows how to give selflessly as well as receive. We want them to think of themselves as persons who can make choices rather than having a victim orientation. They should learn to live for others rather than themselves.

The level of neurological challenge our sons and daughters face will determine the degree to which they can be held accountable for making good choices. However, we do everyone a disfavor if we pamper them and help to shape them into selfish, demanding individuals. In whatever ways they are able, we want to teach them to serve God selflessly.

As we follow Christ, focusing on Him as the center of our lives, we will be able to help our children grow up with wholesome attitudes.

chapter twelve

Accommodating to the Needs of the Special Child and His Family

It becomes a tremendous strength to each of us when our communities surround us with love, understanding and support. Families with special children are no different in this respect. With the heavier responsibility they carry, the gifts of caring that they receive strengthen their hearts and lift up their hands.

Many things can be done to include the special child and his family in the lives of others.

Sanford is a single man who teaches school. Once a week he takes

John, one of the first-grade boys, to his home for a few hours after school is over. Then he takes the child home at suppertime. John is a very hyperactive eight-year-old. Sanford does quite a few things with him. Sometimes they color pictures together, or read books. Occasionally Sanford takes John along as he does his shopping. While Sanford is with John, his mother spends one-on-one time with her preschoolers. (That is difficult to do when John is there.) Sometimes she does something for diversion and relaxation. The doctor has been recommending that she take a walk every day to relieve her high blood pressure and stress levels. Sanford's help makes it possible to fit that in occasionally.

Sam and Lena, neighbors to a family with a very active challenged twelve-year-old, take charge of Amos one Saturday a month. "We all relax and just live a normal life that day," his older brother says. "For once, nobody has to be running after Amos. The break helps us to put our world together again."

Julie had head trauma that changed her from a normal, growing child into an individual requiring constant care. Her parents have a large, growing family of young children. The family's church provides a support group that meets with Julie's parents to discuss any problems that come up. In addition, the three couples in the support group each care for Julie in their homes one morning each week. It has been a great source of support to the home.

Judy is a an older woman who no longer has children of her own to look after during church services. Every other Sunday, she takes care of Grace, a Down's child, so her parents can listen to the message without distraction.

Another simple idea that really takes very little effort is taking a challenged child along with you when you have a two-hour trip to make. For some children, who are thrilled at being able to travel, this provides a very pleasant way to pass a morning. And the interchange provides good social therapy. We all bloom when others take time to love us.

Talk to challenged children in a way that demonstrates to them that you see them as normal persons. Why is it that we feel the need to speak loudly to someone in a wheelchair? Needing a wheelchair means that one has a problem with mobility—not that they have hearing problems. Why do we "talk down" to challenged children? This lack of social discernment hurts not only the child, but his teacher and family members as well.

When Ann wants to do something for her ten-year-old challenged neighbor Kelsie, she invites her over to help make cookies. Kelsie does not have good fine-motor skills. But she is able to hold a shaker to drop sprinkles on the cookies after they are iced. Ann and Kelsie have a great time together. Ann gives Kelsie the gift of knowing that she is valued.

Gerald and Margaret provide respite services to several area families. Once in a while they take supper and spend the evening entertaining the children while the parents have a free night. They also offer care for special children while their parents are gone on trips.

A PARENT'S REQUEST

Dear Community,

Do not avoid talking about our child with us. Do ask how he is doing. We may not answer much in the beginning...or we may say too much! Either way, we remember those who show interest, and can't seem to forget the ones who don't.

Touch us. Touch our child. The gentle hand of my friend on my arm and the warm look in your eyes let me know that you care. A gentle caress on a child's cheek, or having someone spontaneously hold his hand makes him feel "normal." At the beginning of our journey, we feel very different—and very much alone.

Do not tell us how we should or should not feel. We feel whatever there is to feel at the moment… In the early days and months of learning to deal with our problems, we were struggling with raw emotion that was usually near the surface. Each day is still a challenge. And remember the job is ours—24/7.

Do not say, "God only gives us as much as we can handle." We are just trying to survive from one day to the next, especially when we are beginning to find our way. When people give us unwise, well-meant comfort or advice, it makes our load even heavier. And sometimes we don't feel like we're handling anything well at all.

Do not say, "I admire you." or "You are so noble." Unless parents willingly adopt a special-needs child, none of us either planned for or wanted this situation to develop. We don't feel noble. Sometimes we even feel trapped!

Do offer to help. Come sit with my child so I can take a walk in the woods to cool my frazzled resources. Cook a meal or two, and deliver them. Offer to take the siblings to your house for ice cream and pizza.

Be patient with us. It is very hard to work through our grief. In the beginning, all we can see are the things our special children can't or won't be able to do. If we have always been independent or over-achievers ourselves, it may be hard for us to accept your help right away. Please keep on trying, because we desperately desire help to make it. Eventually we will develop grace.

Be sure to acknowledge the siblings of the special-needs child. In the aftermath of a stunning diagnosis, the siblings can get lost in the turmoil. If you come to visit, bring something special for the brothers and sisters too. Be sure to say hello to them. Talk to them before you make a fuss over the child with special needs.

Please don't stare. If our child doesn't look "normal" or acts differently, we are very much aware of it. In fact, that's all we can see at first. Find something positive to say. Something as simple as, "What beautiful eyes!" can be music to our ears. And when you are sharing our deep grief with us, all you need to do is to squeeze our hands meaningfully and say two words, "I'm sorry."

Remember that no matter what kind of disability our child has, he is still a child. He has a desire to be loved and accepted, to be happy and to belong. He needs hugs and laughter, music and friends. He needs you… and so do we.

–Written by a parent

Beatitudes for the Friends of the Handicapped

1. Blessed are those who stop and listen to my chatter. You may not understand much that I say. But I love when people talk to me, because I long for companionship.

2. Blessed are those who take my hand and walk with me when the path is rough. For I easily stumble and grow weary. But thank you too for letting me walk alone when the path is smooth. For I must learn independence.

3. Blessed are those who take the time to tell me about special happenings, for unless you make a special effort to inform me, I remain ignorant.

4. Blessed are those who wait for me. I may be slow, but I appreciate your patience.

5. Blessed are those who are not ashamed to be seen with me in public. I did not choose to be born this way. It could have been you as well.

6. Blessed are those who do not pity me. For I don't want pity. All I want is appreciation and respect for the person that I am. Please be understanding and appreciate the things I have learned to do.

7. Blessed are those who notice my accomplishments, small as they may seem to you. I must work long and hard to learn many of the things you take for granted.

8. Blessed are those who include me in their games. Even though I may not understand the rules, I still like to be included in activities.

9. Blessed are those who think of me as a person who feels love, pain and joy just like you do. When you get down to what really matters, we are all alike.

chapter thirteen

Transitions in the Life of the Special-needs Child

Transitions are hard for many of us. Who likes to have his own plans interrupted? Some changes are trivial. After you have planned to take the children and spend the day with your mother, who likes to find out that your peas will be ready to pick that day? But you console yourself that if you process your peas today, perhaps you can visit your mother on the following day. And things flow smoothly.

Changes are especially hard for the challenged child. For him, fitting into a new setting is particularly difficult. In fact, he will feel that his world is falling apart. He will look to you for reassurance that everything will be all right after all and that he will be able to return to joy again after his pain.

Some children handle change much better if they are informed well in advance. Others will fret and worry as they look at a looming transition—and are better off not knowing very far ahead. You will need to know your child so that you can work with his response pattern.

As you help your child through daily routines, is it generally good to let him know in advance that a change is approaching. Ten minutes before lunch, Maria tells her five-year-old daughter that lunch will soon be ready. Then five minutes later, she alerts her daughter that it is time to put her toys away. With this method, lunch time usually starts on a happy note.

Give the child enough time to register a command or information that you have given him. And work to make sure you understand what the child is trying to communicate to you. This will be particularly challenging if your child is nonverbal.

Zachary is one of the nonverbal children with whom I have worked. One day at home, he kept going to the door and trying to get out. He would not rest even though his mother had told him to stay inside. Finally his mother took him by the hand, and told him to take her where he wanted to go. Zachary promptly seized her hand and headed for the picnic table. Once there, he joyfully grabbed his favorite stuffed doggie that went everywhere with him—and held it up for his mother to see.

Nathan was also nonverbal and could not ask questions. When he could not understand what was going on, he threw temper tantrums. When he was distraught and unhappy, I learned to ponder what had just happened, and what I might need to explain to put him at rest.

One day we had visitors in our classroom. One lady hugged my student Jamie, saying, "I have a little boy at home who looks just like you." But she did not stop to talk to Nathan, and he received no hug. Nathan began getting cranky. However, I did not put two and two together until the next morning—when Nathan arrived at school, still out of sorts. So I took him aside.

"Nathan," I said, "are you thinking about Jamie and the lady who hugged him yesterday? Did you want a hug too?" I watched his eyes for the glimmer of light that might clue me into his thoughts. "That lady had a little boy who looks like Jamie. So she hugged him. But she loved you just as much as she did Jamie. I will hug you right now because you are very special to me. Would you like that?"

Nathan received my hug without any objections. His attitude changed immediately, and he was happy for the rest of the day.

MAJOR TRANSITIONS IN A CHILD'S LIFE

Starting to School

A number of things change when your child goes to school. His life broadens with an amazing increase in relationships. His authority umbrella is also extended. Now there is another person besides his parents to whom he is responsible. His world at home, which was fairly safe and protected, is still the backdrop for his life. But he is now being thrust into new, challenging situations with new people and new places.

Knowing what we are moving into helps to prepare us for the future. In the year before your child starts school, make it a point to visit the lower-grade classroom several times. If the teacher welcomes the idea, you may even be able to send your child to school for a number of half days to work on simple things like coloring.

Invite the new teacher to your home during the summer before your child starts school. Give the two an opportunity to learn to know each other, and do some pleasant activities like taking a walk or playing a game.

If you know your teacher well, she may be willing to orient your child to school by picking him up, taking him to school and showing him around. Your child will feel more comfortable on the first day if he already knows where the bathroom is.

It is a good idea to put the school routine in place a few weeks before school starts. Go to bed more promptly. Get up a little earlier in the morning and eat breakfast in a timely manner, as you would if you were anticipating the school van. For some children, these changes in schedule are devastating if you only begin on the first day of school.

Changing schools is also a threatening experience. There will be a new teacher. And your child will wonder, "Will the children like me? Or will they think I'm dumb?" In the new school, he will be meeting situations he has never encountered before.

It helps if you visit the church you will be going to, and give your child an opportunity to make friendships among the children. Again, learn to know the teacher, and invite her to your house if that is feasible. If the change is taking place in the middle of the year, take your child's books along if that is an option. When a child has been in a tutoring situation, consider asking his present tutor to visit the new teacher with you.

In some situations, the new teacher is willing to spend time tutoring your child over the summer. Do whatever you can to make her feel welcome in your home as an appreciated part of your child's life.

It is unfortunate when two people who are working for the good of a challenged child do not have confidence in one another, do not see situations alike, and do not share the same goals. Yet this often happens with the parents and teachers of special children. Do what you can to be sensitive and open-minded. Parents and teachers can affirm one another. Respect boundaries. While teachers have a priceless gift to offer the child and his family, it is finally the family who will be responsible for their child.

Welcoming a New Baby Into the Family

The coming of a new baby is a very special experience. Yet it can make a special child feel threatened. Who will take care of him while his mother is holding the baby? Where will he fit into the picture? The coming of the new baby will create many kinds of changes in the family structure. Every family member will make sacrifices as the new baby is welcomed and cared for.

Talk about the baby with your child before the baby makes his appearance. Share your excitement with him. Take the child shopping with you, and let him decide if the new crib blanket should be yellow or green. You might also allow your child to help babysit your friend's baby while she goes to the doctor. Or you could visit someone who has a tiny infant.

Some mothers take their children shopping before the new baby comes, to purchase a new doll for them to feed, dress and rock. Little boys can enjoy this too. Teach them to take care of their "baby" just as you will take care of your new treasure when he arrives.

I remember the way my five-year-old nephew described the care of babies and his thoughts about them to me, shortly after his twin sisters were born. "Babies are very breakable, and we must be very careful with them," he explained to me. "We rock them, feed them, and take good care of them—because they can't do anything."

Tell the child that he will be the baby's big brother (or sister), and that the baby is God's gift to the whole family; that the whole family will take special care of this gift. Then move on to talk about another baby that you were so happy to receive when he himself was born, and how much you enjoyed rocking and taking care of him. Show the child his own baby pictures.

"Was I really that cute?" Gloria sparkled, after she and her mother looked through her baby album. "And you will still love me after the baby comes?"

"Dad and I surely will love you after the baby comes!" Gloria's mother exclaimed, as she hugged her. "The baby is God's gift to all of us. We will take care of him together."

Children like to be involved in family plans that involve joy, contributing, and relationships. They love to be a part of a "we" group that is doing something successfully. Make the child feel important by telling him that he can help you take care of the new baby. Tell him that you will need him to get a diaper from the stacker, or to bring a warm blanket to you from the baby's bed. He can help you by cleaning up the toy corner, as well as many other things.

If the baby is born in a hospital, take all the children to see the baby as soon as possible. They will bond to the baby more readily if they are involved in his life from the very beginning.

Moving to a New Home
Here again, communication is the key. Talk about the move you are going to make, and explain the reason for the move to your children. When the move includes a total life change, the adjustment will be much more radical. If you are only moving to a larger house two miles down the road, many things in life will remain the same.

As you discuss your plans, explain what you will be gaining by moving. Give the child a chance to share ideas he has for the new house. Perhaps he can be involved in choosing which room will be his, or the color of the new carpet on the floor. This will make him feel respected and involved in the process.

Sometimes moves are made after crisis have developed. When that occurs, it is important to help our children resolve the stresses and pain that they feel as a result of tragedy or difficulty. Help them to name their losses and the feelings that they have. When we put these sentiments into words, it becomes easier for us to sort through them and deal with them.

Encourage the joy and thrill of adventure as you search out the nooks and crannies of the new barn, the birds that are nesting in the woods, and the flowers that are growing in the flowerbeds. A child's heart has been created to taste life's richness to the full. Yet it must be nurtured.

After the move is made, keep your household routines the same as they were before you moved, if possible. That way something will stay the same, and the old routines will put anchors into the life in the new house. Your child's emotional stability will be reinforced when he is surrounded with solid, familiar habits and patterns.

Adjusting to a Sibling's Marriage

When your child is married, he will walk out of your house and never return in the same manner as when he lived there. While you are adjusting to that loss, your other children will be experiencing their own adjustments. Someone is absent from the daily routine; a relationship has been changed forever. It is true that there may be added blessings from the new in-law, and that in the future there may be nieces and nephews for the child to enjoy. However, for now, a familiar, treasured part of your child's life is changing.

That was especially true for Grace when her sister Brianna married. Grace was adopted when Brianna was thirteen years old. So Brianna had become a daily companion and helper for Grace. When Grace was taunted by another child about her limp, Brianna had held her hand and said, "But I love you just the way you are, Grace. And I'm so glad you can walk. Remember? When you came to us, we all worked very hard to help your leg grow strong enough for you to use it. And I am still so happy about that!"

Now Brianna was moving to South America. There were no promises of frequent visits at her sister's house or of Brianna stopping in now and then. The circles under Grace's eyes grew dark as she watched her sister carefully pack her allotted number of suitcases. Grace was looking solemnly out the living room window one day when her mother approached her. Her mother paused, and put her arms around the ten-year-old.

"What is my little girl thinking about?" she asked quietly.

Grace relaxed against her. "About Brianna going away," she answered. "I will miss her. And there will be nobody to sleep beside me at night."

"I know," her mother answered. "Brianna is going far away. It is all right to feel sad about that. And to cry." For a few minutes, her mother held the sobbing girl in her arms. Then she wiped her tears.

"But do you know what, Grace?" she asked after a bit. "Dad and I have a surprise for you. Did you know that we want to fly down to visit Brianna on your next birthday? And we are going to write letters, and pray for Brianna every day. And she will do the same for us. And sometimes we will talk on the phone. And when we all get to heaven, we can be together without ever leaving again."

Grace nodded. "All the time!" she said.

"Yes," said her mother. "And now I have something I want you to do. Brianna and I want to paint your bedroom walls and put up new curtains this week. You put on your school dress, and all three of us will leave for town. What color would you like the walls to be?"

Grace's mother took care to spend extra time with her, and continued to walk through the experience with Grace. In time, Grace made the adjustment well, and enjoyed the deeper relation she now shared with her mother.

Don't forget your children in their experiences of loss. Talk with them. Walk with them. Help them to accept the losses that cannot be retrieved. And lead them on to the positive things they can use to build. Tomorrow will be another day, and together you can meet it! Remain a strong, continuing presence in the life of your child.

Getting Out of School

When a child no longer goes to school, it means that his life is moving in a different direction. School, with its structure, relationships, and accomplishments is a thing of the past. Sometimes this leaves children feeling lost or inadequate. At that point, we need to focus on the next thing and continue to develop purpose and meaning in life.

As you help your children through this transition, focus on the jobs and satisfying work they will be moving into now. It is a good time to make the young individual responsible for some task that will make him productive and increase his sense of contributing to others. For instance, a fairly capable girl might be given the responsibility to take care of the family's wash. Young men might be taught some viable skills at home. Or they may be ready to take a job in a sheltered situation.

Express appreciation for work that is done well, and you will reinforce your child's development. If your child remains at home with you, make your child an important part of what takes place there. The way you help the child develop at this stage will determine the usefulness of his remaining years. It takes continual effort to teach your son or daughter to be cheerful and unselfish. But fifty years from now, you will be glad that you were committed to teaching the child to live a meaningful life that contributes to others.

Working for Someone Outside the Family

Getting a new job opens up exciting opportunities. It can also be scary. Will the new employer be satisfied with the performance of the young man or lady who comes to help him? Will what that young person has to give be enough?

George and Ruth prepared their son Gregory for his new job by taking him to visit the workplace together. Gregory had known his new boss, a family friend, for years. Gregory, who became challenged after he received a baby shot, watched as the workmen nailed staples into the roofs of the mini barns they were building.

"This is Tom," his new boss said as he introduced a twenty-year-old young man to Gregory. "When you come to work tomorrow, you and Tom will be working together. And if you have any trouble reading instructions or numbers, ask Tom. He will help you."

"The boss tells me you might have some trouble reading," Tom explained, as he visited with Gregory later. "I've had a lot of trouble with dyslexia in my early years of school. So I know exactly how it feels to have that problem. If you have any trouble, we'll find the way through. I think we'll make a good team!"

Gregory laughed and relaxed. The next day went well. In time, Gregory became a valued worker at the mini barn shop.

You may be acquainted with workshops that are geared for handicapped people, where they can work and receive a small paycheck. Make your child feel competent by telling him that now he has a job like his big brothers and sisters do. Help him establish goals for worthwhile things he can do with the money he will earn, as well as saving ten percent. And you will be teaching him money management.

Meeting a Death Within the Family

Margaret put down the phone and pondered silently, as tears streamed down her cheeks. Her father had passed away. How would she tell Jason, her twelve-year-old challenged son—who had spent hours with his grandfather? Only yesterday the two had been tramping through the woods behind their house.

Her father had always been their support and encourager since Jason, her Down's baby, had been born. He had cheered the loudest when Jason was able to read his reading story without help for the first time. It was he who had persevered until Jason was able to ride his bike without training wheels. And after Jason's own father passed away, she and Jason had moved into a house on the home farm. Then her father had stepped in to become Jason's father.

The door opened, and Jason entered. "Can I go over to Pap-Paps'?" he asked. But seeing his mother's face, he stopped and looked troubled. "Why you cry?" he asked, patting her shoulder. "It be okay."

"You're right, Jason," Margaret answered. "But I have something very sad to tell you. Grandma just called to say that Grandpa has gone to heaven to be with Jesus. I am very sad. But Grandpa is happy now."

"My Grandpa die?" Jason asked disbelievingly.

"Yes." Margaret put her arm around the chubby shoulders. "A horse kicked his head when he was at Uncle Jakes', and he went to be with Jesus. He left his body here, and he moved to heaven. So Grandpa is very happy now. But we are sad. Because we will miss him."

"My kitten die," said Jason. "Dead. No play. I cry. My Grandpa die? Mean horse! I want my Grandpa!"

Then he buried his face against his mother's shoulder and cried bitterly. As he would slowly learn, his grandfather, like the dead kitten, would no longer play with him.

Death is so final, so invincible, and so solemn. And our hearts weep. Grieving is a process that cannot be avoided, if our hearts are to live with passion again. How do we teach our children to process grief so that they will be able to move on with life again?

It is important for children to understand what caused the death of a loved one. If illness precedes the death, try to spend time with the family member before death. Teach your children that even though we live on the earth now, God created us to live in heaven with Him— forever. So the deceased loved one has truly gone home. And because of Jesus' love for us, someday we will go to meet our loved one there.

Acknowledge the grief the child feels. It is valid. Encourage him to share his fears, his anger, and his anxieties. Then help him give them all to God, who promises to come to us with healing when we seek His face. Sadness and struggling is a normal part of grieving.

Margaret and Jason made a scrapbook about the things Jason and his grandfather had shared. When Jason longed to tramp through the woods with his Grandpa, he and his mother covered a page with a picture of trees, people walking on a path together, and tear drops. Frequently, after Jason would cry on the couch, he would stand up again and tell his mother, "I make page about Grandpa." And after he had worked on the page for a while, he would get up quietly and go out to play again.

One of Jason's most treasured possessions is a pillow his mother and grandmother made for him from some of the clothes his grandfather used to wear. He takes it to bed with him every night. Some nights he looks at the shirt fabrics and cries. But more often now, he smiles and remembers the happy times. What a precious Grandfather he has had—someday he will see him again.

"My Grandpa love me!" he exclaims.

chapter fourteen

Teaching Self Care and Home Usefulness

We help a child develop…
- · By challenging, not coddling.

- · By letting go of his hand, or he will never realize his reach.

- · By not moving all the mountains before him, lest he never reach his summit.

–Anonymous

When we teach a challenged child to care for himself and to become useful at home, we have given the child a tremendous gift. Care providers will seek to understand the child's challenge, and they will find ways to make him as independent and productive as possible.

What one child can do will vary tremendously from another.

We have a greater feeling of self worth when we know that we can do something well and that we are contributing to a family or school group. A child can learn to contribute even in small ways.

Normally, do not do things for the child that you know he can do for himself. This will require lots of patience on your part as you wait for the child to complete the task. But never forget that learning self care always boosts one's self-confidence.

A child who does not have verbal skills but could master sign language should be taught to communicate with his hands. Nonverbal individuals can also be taught to give cues that those around them can understand. If the nonverbal child has no control over his body, perhaps he can tell you he is thirsty by directing his eyes to a picture of a cup on the wall. Be creative. Communication is the gateway into the soul and frees the spirit to fly.

If the child is able to talk on the phone, teach him good telephone manners. I let my special-needs students practice by calling home to give their parents a message various times. Talking on the phone also teaches the child to interact with others in a healthy way. A child can also be taught to respond to the kindness of others by making thank-you cards for them. Most children could do at least a part of the work if a family member helps.

Allow the child to do what he can for himself. Or at least to help in the process. As you teach him a new skill, such as brushing his teeth, be nearby to offer your assistance when it is necessary. If possible, make yourself less necessary all the time.

Reaching even small milestones takes tremendous work for those to whom it does not come easily. Acknowledge the achievements the child learns. Commend him. Honest words of praise are balm to our struggling hearts and encourage us to take the next steps.

Live exuberantly! Establish reasons for living, and live your life with the fixed purpose to reach those goals. Find your center in Jesus Christ, and walk with God through every day. Our children often absorb their purpose for living—or lack of it—from what they see us model.

If you know the child is capable of a task, don't give him the opportunity to decide whether or not he can accomplish it. Move briskly and cheerfully into the task with him. Show him what to do. Then help him learn to do the task himself. This is the task of a parent.

Your home rules will be different for your challenged child than they were/are for his siblings. You will choose a pattern that is right for him, one that his abilities will support. For instance, if his older brothers were allowed to drive a tractor by a certain age, that probably would not apply to a challenged child.

Be prepared to use multiples of the discipline your other children required. This is the journey of training a special child, so we should expect the extra work and not be surprised. Provide structure and control that will help to place security in his life, and the discipline needs you face will be lessened. A calm, firm, consistent approach will steady you as you train and discipline him. Keep in mind that some of the methods you use with your challenged child will be different from the ones that work well for his unchallenged siblings. But discipline must be there.

When you can, provide the special things that bring delight to your challenged child's heart. For Audrey, that delight is an ice-cream cone. Benjamin loves his farm equipment collection, and a new piece is very carefully put into its own place in the lineup. If siblings become jealous at the attention, ask them if they would like to trade places in life with their challenged brother or sister. Explain that there will be things they can do that their challenged sibling cannot, and sometimes he will have privileges that they will not have. To some degree, we do treat special children a bit special.

Before you set out to reach a goal with your child, make sure that he has reached the development level that will enable him to cooperate with you. For instance, wait to teach the child to tie his shoe until he has learned to use sewing cards or has strung beads.

Teachers should alternate activities so that the child's resources will not be maxed out in the school schedule. Rather than having all gross motor skill activities in one period, it would be better to spread them out so that only one gross motor skill is taught in one period.

It is good to involve other qualified people to create priorities that will help the child. Has your child ever been evaluated, with a list of goals set up for him? It is helpful to return to your evaluator on a regular basis so that you can keep pace with the needs of your child. It is also encouraging, for both you and the child, to be given affirmation that your child has made gains.

Following is a list of personal hygiene tasks that you will want to help your child learn, if possible.

- Learning how to use a handkerchief. Teach him how to blow his own nose. I have used ping pong balls to teach a student to blow his nose—by having him blow the ball across his desk with his mouth shut.

- Learning how to take a bath.

- Shampooing his own hair.

- Learning how to dress himself.

- Learning to brush his teeth. (You might consider a battery-powered toothbrush.) I have found that the most difficult part of this process is to teach the child to spit the water out when he is done.

- Tucking in shirttails. Mothers, it may help if you give your sons pants with elastic in the waist as they learn this skill.

- Keeping socks pulled up.

- Putting on a coat. It may be helpful to lay the coat open on the floor, and have the child stand with the collar next to his feet. This helps the child figure out where each arm will go. He then slips his arms into the coat and flips it over his head. Presto—the coat is on correctly.

- Zipping his coat.

- Opening and closing buttons.

- Tying a scarf or hood.

- Tying shoes. Using a brown and a green string, teach children to make the first easy tie. Then they should make a loop with the green string. Then the bunny (the brown string) runs around the tree and dives into his hole. After that he sticks his head up, and the child grabs his ears (both loops—the bunny and the tree) and pulls them tight as he sticks his head out of the hole.

Teach good table manners.

It will be a blessing to everyone in the child's life, including himself, if he can learn good table manners. I had the children help bring in food for a meal together twice a month so that we would have the opportunitiy to work on table manners, along with setting the table and washing dishes.

- Chewing with his mouth closed. This is a tough one, but keep trying.

- Not talking with his mouth full of food.

- Not drinking from plates.

- Not licking plates or knives.

- Using his napkin when his mouth or fingers are dirty. I found that using cloth napkins or washcloths worked quite well with my school students.

- Not taking food from anyone else's plate. I punished children for this offense. If something delectable was taken from another person, I made the child return something special.

- Asking for food to be passed. Don't allow the child to get up from the table or reach across the table to get what he wants. Be sure to ask the nonverbal children what they would like.

- Staying seated until you are excused. This is hard for some children. The penalty for my school children was that they could not come back for dessert if they left the table before that.

- Always remembering to thank the person who made the food.

These are crafts your child may enjoy.

- Spool knitting and making hot pads. These are worthwhile projects. They also prepare the child to move into circular knitting to make caps, or straight knitting to make scarves.

- Stringing baby beads. You might need to lay the pattern out for your child. Different colors of beads can be kept in separate boxes.

- Cross-stitching dresser scarves, making quilt blocks for cribs or comforters, or creating pillows. You may need to begin their sewing skills by using sewing cards. If you are teaching the child to embroider, try to teach him to thread his own needles and knot his own thread.

Even younger children can often master these jobs.

- Hanging up towels, washcloths and diapers. They will love to have their own clothespin bag and wash basket. We washed the rags weekly at school to give my students practice in hanging up clothes on a line.

- Taking dry clothing off the line and bringing it in. For an incentive, you might hide a small piece of candy or an eraser in the pile of clothes for the child to find and keep. They can sort the dry, unfolded clothes into like piles in wash baskets—towels in one, shirts in another, and so on. If the items of clothing are marked, the child may be able to sort them and put them in the correct bedroom.

- Doing Saturday work. You can make a picture chart or list, and offer the child a small reward such as a penny, a sticker or a Smartie for having completed a job. You can also use a bigger surprise at the end—whatever works best for you and your child.

- Feeding weeds from the garden to the chickens. They can also carry water to the chickens, or give them two scoops of feed.

- Shelling peas or breaking green beans. For the smallest children, you may want to give them a plastic container with a hole in the lid, so they are kept sanitary.

- Helping with dishes. Start with rinsing. Let them dry dishes, as well as washing them.

- Ironing. Some children will be capable of handling an iron that is turned on low to iron hankies.

- Peeling potatoes. You might need to supply a Band-Aid once in a while. But that can happen to anyone.

- Mowing the yard, if doing so does not become a safety issue. This, of course, will depend on the capability of the child.

- Pulling weeds in the garden and flower beds, with supervision.

- Learning arithmetic. While you work, send him for three potatoes, have him pull eight weeds, and so on. If numerals are not meaningful to the child, have him keep track by putting buttons in a bowl or using some similar method.

- Scrubbing veggies. When you have a lot of veggies, put a tub out in the yard and let the children have fun.

- Canning. Maybe the child can slice the cucumbers for a jar of pickles, and put his name on the jar. What fun to eat them!

- Filling the wheelbarrow or wagon to feed the calves.

- Sweeping and vacuuming the floors.

Be on the alert for what I call "controller signs."
These can begin even in a younger child.
- Soiling themselves.

- Refusing to use the toilet.

- Vomiting.

- Crying (for older children) or refusing to wipe their noses.

- Exhibiting demanding social manners that keep others' attention locked in.

- Saying "good-bye" again, again, again and again.

Give the child certain tasks that he is always responsible to do. He could—
- Gather eggs.

- Take dirty plates from the table to the kitchen.

- Empty all the trash cans in the house into a garbage bag.

- Set the table before each meal.

- Feed pets.

- Gather the laundry.

- Polish the shoes.

- Get the mail, if the box is on your side of the road.

- Sweep out the vehicle.

- Wash cars.

- Wash windows.

- Make beds.

- Do simple cooking with recipe cards.

School teachers have many opportunities to teach the child useful, tidy habits.

Focus on the following:

- Hanging his coat on a hook. I remember working with one of my students for months on this skill. But he finally learned.

- Pulling up his zipper. Even if you need to start it, he can probably finish it.

- Putting his lunch box on the shelf. Anything that you teach the child will assist the parents in helping their child.

- Getting his own crayons and books out of his desk. (Does he do what you ask—immediately?)

- Learning to put on his own shoes or boots. Velcro can be a good option here. But if you are teaching the child to tie his shoes, consider having two different colors on each shoestring. You can also start with strips of material that are easier to handle.

- Getting his sandwich out of the bag. Teach him to close zip-lock bags.

- Opening his own food containers.

chapter fifteen

Overcoming Specific Obstacles

Reactive Attachment Disorder (RAD)

RAD occurs in some children who experience trauma in situations where bonding should have occurred. Because the child has been abandoned, or feels that he has been abandoned, he withdraws from close relationships to avoid more pain. This is especially true where mother figures are involved. When the mother bond is not established, the child is lacking the most important link that supports all other development.

RAD is commonly found in children who have been given for adoption at birth by their biological mothers. It can also happen in situations where the birth process has been very difficult, or when the baby is kept in NICU for weeks when he cannot be held or cuddled. When a baby is separated from his mother early in life, he loses the security of the attachment he developed to his mother while he was in her womb.

These children are often dumped into the fight-or-flight mode. We often find that they have retained infant reflexes that need to be integrated. When we have accomplished that goal, we are able to help retrain the brain and fill in the missing gaps.

I have worked with several children who have done therapy for RAD when they were three or four. In working with them, it was necessary to go back through normal stages of babyhood, such as drinking from a bottle or wearing diapers. Sometimes they needed to return to sucking their thumbs, even though the habit had already disappeared. Though the journey was difficult for all involved, they were able to rebound well and to bond securely.

Fetal Alcohol/Drug Syndrome (FAS)

Children with FAS have suffered brain damage because their birth mother ingested alcohol and/or drugs during the pregnancy. The baby is born with tremendous challenges. As the tiny baby struggled to survive in his mother's womb, his body was forced into the fight-or-flight mode for self-preservation. Tragically, the part of the brain that helps us understand cause and effect, the corpus callosum, is severely damaged in these tiny ones. The corpus callosum is an important aid in having a conscience, since it allows a child to associate punishment with bad behavior.

An FAS child is easily frustrated by normal happenings, and is overwhelmed on a regular basis. His frustration makes his own life miserable. Caring for these children becomes very challenging, since they go into rages and become uncontrollably angry at the least provocations.

Derek came into my office. As his parents faithfully did therapy with him, he became much calmer. However, when we stopped therapy, he reverted to his old behavior. We discovered that he would need to do five minutes of therapy per day on a continual basis to support his corpus callosum. This enabled him to function with a conscience and to live more successfully.

Cerebral Palsy

Cerebral palsy is a condition that results when the motor part of the brain has been damaged. It can result from birth trauma or from a head injury. These children have trouble moving their arms and legs, and are often stiff. Doing therapy that keeps the muscles more toned is helpful.

One of my clients was a little boy with a fairly advanced case of cerebral palsy, who found it hard to use his arms and legs. However, he was fully determined that he would walk. So he did therapy for several years and accomplished his goal. However, he still found that using a three-wheeled bike or a wheelchair worked best for covering long distances.

Down's Syndrome

Down's children have broad ranges of abilities that can be developed. As we work with Down's children, a lot can be done to help them function at their highest potential as adults.

Because a Down's child has low muscle tone, it is important to focus on strengthening muscle groups—and to do so early and consistently. It is advisable to have a reputable health care provider evaluate the child so that the parents will know what they are working with. Older siblings help in the process by holding the child in their arms and jiggling him. This develops the child's sense of balance as well as his muscle tone.

The brain can be likened to a wheel with many intersecting gears—

where all the areas involved need to develop and work in synergy for normal brain function. In normal development, the lower part of the brain develops first. Then the higher levels follow, using the lower part as a foundation. So it is important that we do the marine crawl before we crawl on our hands and knees, and that we crawl before we walk. We follow this pattern as we work with Down's children.

Preemies

The preemie begins life with a disadvantage because he is born before his body and mind have reached the normal stages of development for a newborn. During the last two months of the pregnancy, the movements of the mother help to develop the vestibular system in her unborn child. So a child who is born early will need therapy.

One way to provide this is to sit on an office chair to feed your baby. Turn slowly in one direction, then in the other. Every time you pick the baby up, turn him gently this way and that, tipping his head up and down, as you hold him in your arms.

Tummy time is even more important for the preemie than it is for a child born with a full-term pregnancy. Give your preemie lots of tummy time, now and again, through the course of each day. I cannot emphasize this enough.

Preemies need lots of touching as well. Play with your baby's tiny fingers and toes. Massage his head, body, arms and legs gently. As you rub his head, you will help develop brain function. It is interesting that parents naturally rub or pat a baby's or toddler's head. Doing so aids a normal part of development.

If your child is in a hospital that allows kangaroo care, it will be a great blessing to your child. When this is done, the mother wears a baby carrier against her chest, where the baby's skin touches her own. This provides for the baby's needs much better than being isolated in a sterile cubicle—where he cannot bond.

C-Section

A baby born by C-section is at a serious disadvantage. When I think of the human birth, I think of a butterfly who struggles as he emerges from his cocoon. Without that struggle, his wings never develop properly. In the same way, the normal birth process provides a series of developmental stages that develop the brain and aid the child as he enters the world of gravity. So when it becomes necessary to do a C-section to save the baby's or the mother's life, it is important to do therapy to fill in the missing gaps of development in the brain.

One of the most important things we can do is to help the child develop a strong sense of body mapping. We accomplish this by rubbing the child's arms and legs, his head, his body—and his little fingers and toes. There is indeed a good reason for the little finger and toe games we play with our little ones.

C-section babies often like and need the pressure of being wrapped firmly in a soft blanket. We call this swaddling. We should also hold these babies firmly in our arms, since they need to feel pressure.

Adoption

Children who come from hard places in life are very vulnerable. A child who has been adopted has already encountered major difficulty at one or more levels. One of the major issues every adopted child faces is that the mother bond with his birth mother has been broken. To do well, he will need to reattach to another mother figure.

As the birth mother of an adopted child moves through her pregnancy, there is a high probability that she is stressed. She may not be supported emotionally or physically. She may not be eating nourishing food for herself and the baby. Any kind of stress the mother experiences during this time will leave neurochemical marks on her baby. Mothers who are anxious or depressed give birth to infants who have higher levels of stress chemicals and alterations of brain activity.

Prenatal exposure to substances such as drugs or alcohol bring a lot of undesirable changes in cognition and behavior. We can work with some of these during therapy. However, the child will face many difficulties in life because of his birth mother's unwise choices.

Birth trauma can also be a large risk factor for a newborn. Any kind of brain hemorrhaging can cause learning issues and behavioral problems. Medical procedures, which save lives, often compromise the neurological systems of children, resulting in learning disabilities.

Another risk factor is hospitalization early in life, where the child is separated from his mother. NICU care, surgeries, and hospitalizations after accidents create particular trauma when they occur in the infant stages of a child's life.

Trauma, abuse and neglect are common themes in the life of an adopted or foster child. Unfortunately, these conditions leave definite marks on the child.

Neglect is a strong factor with these children as well. While neglect may seem less damaging than abuse to us, that is not necessarily the case. Abuse sends a loud, clear message that says, "I do not like you." However, a neglected child is being fed the lie, "You don't exist." Even after the child has been moved into a loving, safe environment, he is constantly overshadowed by the lie that he has been fed early in life.

These children often have multiple foster placements, each making their responses more complex.

We work with many adoptive families. With therapy, we are able to bless the children by working with them neurologically. We routinely rejoice with parents as their children improve. We are blessed to be able to nurture the little lambs whom Jesus loves.

May every adoptive family take courage from God's Word. The work of receiving adoptive children into our homes is God's. We are not responsible to guarantee an outcome. Rather, we offer a gift and an opportunity. And we commit our little ones to God.

"Suffer the little children to come unto me, and forbid them not: for of such is the kingdom of God" (Mark 10:14).

"Inasmuch as ye have done it unto one of the least of these my brethren, ye have done it unto me" (Matthew 25:40).

chapter sixteen

Pregnancy and Birthing Issues

Pregnancy is a time of deep excitement. You are holding a tiny treasure under your heart. As you think of all the possibilities of interacting with that child, you reach out with an eager heart. What a humbling realization it is, one that fills your heart with joy, to know that God is working through you and your husband to create yet another eternal soul!

What should we consider as we think of pregnancy and birthing issues?

Maintaining a Good Lifestyle

Eating for your baby begins long before your pregnancy test reads positive. A mother needs to be eating well for several years before she carries a little one. The food we eat affects the DNA we will give to our children. Eating responsibly is one of the gifts every parent should offer his legacy. For even as your little girls are born, they already carry the essence from which their eggs will be made. Good genetics that have been fostered by nourishing food for three generations can be undone by poor eating habits in the fourth generation. This means we have a strong accountability to God for the way we affect the temples in which He will dwell.

Mothers should eat lots of good fats during pregnancy. (See Chapter Two: Foods that Aid Development.) As the baby's brain and central nervous system develop, he will need a steady supply of fat, which forms 60 percent of the human brain. You will also want to eat lots of chemical-free vegetables, and meats that are produced without chemicals or hormones. Remember to eat protein often throughout the day. Your baby needs lots of building blocks as his body develops. Use A2A2 raw milk products to provide good fats, proteins and calcium. Avoid all white sugar, white flour and foods that have no nutritional value.

If you find yourself gaining too much weight, cutting out all the unhealthy parts of your diet will help. Never cut out fats that your baby needs to develop a strong brain. Instead, plan to lose weight after the baby is born. Avoid water pills, even if you are retaining fluids, since these will stress the baby. You can expect to lose the fluids naturally.

Every woman in her childbearing years should be on a good multi-vitamin. Forget the cheap brands that do not contain what your body is needing, and purchase a quality product. We know that farm animals need real quality in their supplements if we are to turn a good profit. Why then would we choose to put a mother's or baby's health at risk by buying the cheap, ineffective brands?

Even before she is married, a woman should be taking folic acid as a supplement. This practice should continue as long as she is in her childbearing years. Folic acid is very important in preventing abnormalities in children, both physically or neurologically. These include spina bifida, cleft palate and other neurological disorders. The nervous system of the baby is being developed in the first two months of pregnancy.

Drink plenty of water. Remember that our bodies are made largely of water. It is recommended that a pregnant woman drinks at least two to three quarts of water per day. My midwife told me to have a gallon jar sitting on the kitchen counter. When I drank a cup of water, I was to put the same amount in the jar. This tends to stop the problem of somehow thinking that we having been drinking more water than we really have.

Grace stopped drinking all sugar drinks, and a healthy pregnancy weight gain was easier to maintain. Most of her fluids were provided by plain water. She also drank milk, as well as caffeine-free teas. It was a good habit that Grace adopted permanently.

Exercising well is another part of a good pregnancy lifestyle. Use gentle movements that prevent falls, and avoid twisting. But stay on the move. Walking is an excellent exercise for our total persons. And as you do, pray for the little one you are carrying.

The thoughts you think and the way you view life are impacting your child. He is already learning to know you. Fetuses know whether or not they are wanted. The unborn child knows when his mother is eagerly awaiting him. He also knows when he is unwelcome. The development of his central nervous system will be hampered if he does not sense a warm reception.

Sleep is very important. Arrange your schedule so that you can have full nights. And take a nap in the afternoon while the children are resting. Your body uses sleep hours to build and repair itself in a way that will bless your tiny, developing baby. You will also be able to function better and preserve your own health (which is also important).

X-rays, Ultrasounds, Dopplers, Cell Phones and Baby Monitors

The effects of X-rays on our bodies accumulate during our lifetimes. Avoid all X-rays while you are pregnant. And remember that the sperm of a man and the eggs of a woman are at risk each time an X-ray is taken.

When an ultrasound is done, it raises the temperature of your unborn child's intracellular liquid, as well as the mother's amniotic fluid (the fluid in the womb). What you are doing is raising the temperature of your baby's body with sound waves. In some respects ultrasound compares with microwaving.

Does this matter? Unfortunately, ultrasound was not tested on humans before its debut as a standard medical option. So we and our children are the guinea pigs. However, studies on mice show that their brains are changed after exposure, and that cellular activity is also affected.

In most cases, it cannot be proven that ultrasounds are helpful for any practical purpose. The world uses ultrasound to discover if the baby has abnormalities. In that event, the mother can choose if she wishes to abort her baby. (After the baby has been aborted, it may be found to be a normal fetus.) However, the Christian woman who values the sacred life within her womb does not even consider abortion.

The American College of Obstetricians and Gynecologists, the American College of Radiology, and the US Government's Preventive Services Task Force all caution against routine ultrasound screening for low-risk pregnancies. The FDA cautions, "While ultrasound has been around for many years, expectant women and their families need to know that long-term effects of repeated ultrasound exposures on the fetus are not fully known."

When there are higher-risk pregnancies, we are wise to ask questions. Some studies link growth retardation to frequent ultrasounds. Since you are not planning to abort your baby in any case, how will ultrasound affect your struggling child? Is it wise to place a high-risk fetus in a situation that changes the brains and cells of lab animals?

Ultrasound use is not compulsory in the United States. And if your doctor pressures you to have an ultrasound, to protect himself from possible liability claims, you have the right to choose another doctor. If you do decide to do an ultrasound, insist that your technician uses the lowest power that is effective—and for the shortest amount of time. Also be aware that when ultrasounds are used in one pregnancy, all the children born afterward will be affected. For when you ultrasound the child you are carrying, you are also exposing the eggs that will produce your remaining children.

From a personal standpoint, I have learned what I can expect to see when a child whose mother has had frequent ultrasounds comes into my office. I am not surprised to see yet another hyperactive child, stuck in the fight-or-flight mode, who cannot concentrate.

Doppler fetoscopes are ultrasound devices. Doppler devices expose fetuses to powerful doses of sound waves. One minute of doppler exposure has the same blast of energy that comes from a thirty-five minute ultrasound. One midwife suggests that a better way to check on the baby's health is by counting to see if there are ten distinct fetal movements between 9:00 a.m. and 3:00 p.m. That will not impact your baby in any negative way.

Wireless connections present in our homes affect the environments in which we and our families live. Wireless phones that connect to a central land line based phone may be more harmful to your child than cell phones. There is a price to pay for all the fancy technology that is available today.

L. Lloyd Morgan (Senior science fellow at Environmental Health Trust) headed a study regarding microwave radiation (MWR) on children. This same issue is also referred to as electromagnetic field irradiation (EMF). Morgan's group found that children and unborn babies face a higher rate for bodily damage from MWR than adults do. The MWR factor applies to all the wireless devices that are in use today. If there is no cord—beware!

The rate at which children and fetuses absorb MWR is higher for various reasons. Their brain tissues are more absorbent, and their skulls are thinner. In addition, the relative size of their bodies is also smaller. Fetuses are particularly at risk because MWR exposure leads to degeneration of the sheath that God has placed around brain neurons for our protection. Studies have shown that the bone marrow of children absorbs ten times more MWR than their adult counterparts do.

Swedish researchers have observed young rats after they were exposed to a cell phone for only two hours. They found leakage of albumin from the blood brain barrier of the rats. Long term exposure of this kind of radiation destroys nerve cells in the basal ganglia, the hypo campus and the cortex of the brain. When we see attention and learning disorders, these areas of the brain have usually become affected. Since the use of wireless devices is becoming more rampant, we will probably see even more neurological issues developing in the emerging generation.

If you cannot avoid MWR for yourself or your child, keep the devices you are using as far away as possible. Strictly limit the time you use a cell phone. Morgan recommends that holding a cell phone six inches away from your ear will give you a 10,000 fold reduction of the risk factor. Remember that a cell phone is always radiating if it is not turned off. A pregnant woman should never store her cell phone in a pocket against her abdomen. And a mother should never use her cell phone while she is nursing her baby.

Wireless baby monitors are also damaging our babies. If you chose to use one, keep the unit as far away from your baby as possible. If you are having trouble finding a wired unit, check out the Foscam brand. Even if you can only find a wireless Foscam version, you can make it wired by purchasing an ethernet over AC adapter, and plugging into the ethernet jack on the back of your wireless model. Do not place a monitor in your baby's bed.

The Pregnancy

Talk to your baby, even before he is born. Your developing child is listening to your voice and loves to hear it. Sing. Speak gentle, loving words. And focus on maintaining a calm, trusting attitude as you relate to life. Every father should be an active support who relieves his wife of unnecessary stress as the family awaits the coming of the child. Fetuses relate to stress by developing retained reflexes. When this happens they are not able to assist in the birth with the reflexes that should be in place. And the child's further neurological development is impeded.

If a mother is on bedrest at any time in her pregnancy, there will be a repercussion. The mother's movements within the last two months are especially important for vestibular development. If the baby has missed this development, the mother should sit on an office chair, turning back and forth, as she feeds her baby. She should also turn the baby this way and that as she holds the newborn in her arms. (See Preemies in Chapter Fifteen.)

If your preemie is in a hospital that allows kangaroo care, it will be a great blessing to your child. When this is done, the mother wears a baby carrier against her chest, where the baby's skin touches her own. This provides for the baby's needs much better than being isolated in a sterile cubicle—where he is alone and afraid, and cannot bond. In a cubicle, he cannot be with the mother he had been living with for months.

The Birth Experience

The total birth experience will affect you and your baby in many ways. Having a baby is a very natural, normal thing—not a medical crisis. Plan for a situation where you can deliver the baby in a stress-free environment. Then relax and let things progress.

As the baby's birth progresses, a problem may occur if the cord catches around the baby's neck. This causes the oxygen flow to be broken. The baby's brain needs a continuous flow of oxygen. This problem also causes tightness in the baby's neck muscles.

A birth that proceeds too quickly or too slowly both present the baby with neurological issues. Holding back when a baby is ready to be born is also a bad thing for the baby.

Sometimes medical interventions are used when a birth proceeds slowly. These include the use of Pitocin to bring on more or stronger contractions, suction tools or forceps to help pull the baby through the birth canal, or doing a C-section.

Geneva holds her baby gently in her arms, though her eyes are sad as she looks at Sally's misshapen head. "Joan," she says, "when I asked the doctor to use a suction tool after I got tired of pushing, I didn't know that I was hurting my baby. What exercises can I do to help Sally now?"

If your labor is progressing slowly and the need to use Pitocin is being discussed, ask your health provider to break your water instead. That may be all that is needed.

As we talk to the mothers of our clients, we see a direct relationship between the use of Pitocin, both in the amount used and the length of time it was administered, and the neurological damage the child has sustained. Many midwives feel that there is little reason to use Pitocin before the baby is born. (It may be used to stop hemorrhaging after the birth.) The schedules of health care providers are really not that important.

When suction tools and forceps are used to help deliver the child, the baby's skull bones are sometimes pulled out of place. This affects the way his brain will work. (Notice whether or not your baby's head has been misshapen.) If this has occurred, do a lot of gentle massage on the baby's head. And take him to a reputable chiropractor, who adjusts the bones of the skull, as soon as possible. Sometimes a baby will not be able to latch on well to nurse because his jaw was dislocated during birth. Any time the brain becomes bruised, the baby experiences head trauma.

During a too-long, slow labor, there is also a tendency for the baby's cranial bones to get stuck. A reputable chiropractor who adjusts skull bones is also needed in this case.

If the baby's cord is pinched during delivery, or if he is not breathing well after birth, a crisis exists that may result in brain damage. (See cerebral palsy in Chapter Fifteen.) Lack of oxygen to any part of the brain causes damage.

C-sections disadvantage the baby in several ways. Coming through the birth canal helps the baby to develop a good body map. When the baby is not born vaginally, or if he is born too fast, he will not have a good reference as to where he is in space. Then his brain will spend lots of its energy trying to provide balance and coordination. When this happens, the brain has less potential to address other issues.

The tremendous boom in C-sections that we currently see seems related to ultrasound and an increase in other medical interventions. There are times when medical intervention becomes necessary for the well-being of either the mother or the child. The problem arises when interventions that are only needed in crisis situations become the "gold standard" for normal medical care.

※ ※ ※

As you give birth to the little one your heart has already come to love, rest in the care of your heavenly Father, who loves both you and your tiny treasure infinitely. We need not live in fear. As we look proactively at the options that are open to us and make wise choices, we are doing our part. And we cast our care upon the Lord, who created and sustains His creation.

Neither should we live with guilt when our children have neurological damage. Some decisions surrounding pregnancy and delivery are out of our control. And when we would redo a situation differently if we could, even that we need to cast upon the Lord who forgives us—and makes good from our mistakes. For God is working with human clay. Walk humbly with God, and you will move into sustaining peace and inner joy.

If you have a special child, receive him with full acceptance. There are many tools available to you that can help him. We live in an imperfect world, where God has a special purpose for every child He sends to us. In heaven, your child will know no limitations of any kind. We long for the day of our full redemption. *"Even so, come, Lord Jesus!"* (Revelation 22:20).

chapter seventeen

Parental Attitudes That Build

Be a competent person in your own right.

Before we can take care of someone else, we must first be able to care for ourselves. Before we can provide security for another when life is difficult, we must first establish our own emotional security. The ability to bear children does not give us these skills. It is therefore necessary that we are personally mature before we become parents.

The center peg of our personal security must rest in Christ. Then when the winds blow and our ships are tossed at sea, we will have the presence of Christ as our resource. We then find that it is not the winds that determine our destination, but rather the set of our sails. Christ has promised to be with us to the end—and for the born again Christian, our destination is heaven!

We must build our lives around the truth of God's Word. Otherwise we will establish our lives around personal goals that operate on the basis of lies we come to believe. When our point of security begins with being certain that God loves us completely, and that we are safe and approved of when we order our lives according to His plan for our lives—we are personally secure.

When we are approval-oriented, we believe that other people are able to determine our value or lack of it, by the way (we imagine) they evaluate us. This is not only a very foolish response, but one that dishonors God. Because we live our lives to please others when we are approval-oriented, we make them our idols. What a ridiculous loss!

If we live with approval orientation, we will teach our children to live the same way. Then it will become more important to them to make a good impression on the neighbors than to do God's will. And they will do sinful things to fit with their peers instead of doing what is right. To live with approval orientation means that we live under the scourge of guilt and shame by our own choice, when it is needless to do so. And our lives are stifled.

Neither can we establish our own identity or emotional security on our children's behavior and worth. We are each our own persons. When we stand before God, each person will stand alone. If we see our children's lives as extensions of our own, then when they fail, we will be resentful and defensive. Rather, we must set ourselves at liberty from our sons and daughters so that we can help them objectively.

We cannot be good parents if we expect our children to fulfill our lives. Instead, we must be givers. Parenting is all about thinking of our children's good above our own. It means to look at issues in terms of their best interests.

Be a vital, living fountain in your child's life.
I think of Anna, who wore knee pads and crawled with her son

Chad as he did his therapy. While they were crawling, they laughed and talked. Anna filled many of these shared crawling times by telling Chad Bible stories that he will always remember.

"I always enjoyed crawling with Chad," Anna says brightly. "It became a special time for us to share together. Who knows? I may have brightened my own mind while Chad was developing his."

Anna has the fountain of life flowing within her. She attacks life as it comes to meet her. And there is joy in her heart that splashes onto Chad. You can see it in his face when you talk to him.

A father has a very special role to fill in the life of his child. For as he protects, blesses, nurtures, and makes his child accountable, he establishes the child's concept of God. Failing to be an able leader, not protecting the child, speaking angry words, or acting out of selfishness will tarnish the God concept in the child's mind. This requires that a father live for God and his family rather than for himself. What a privilege it is for a man to fill the father role and shape his children's hearts to be ready to receive God.

Maintain healthy boundaries in your home.

Every good parent desires a relationship with his child. What are the balances of boundaries and relationships as we teach and train our children?

True love does what is needed to secure the best for the child. As we look at God the Father, we find a beautiful pattern that parents must also follow. When God offers a relationship to mankind, He establishes the boundaries. And when we honor those boundaries, we are given unfathomable blessings.

Every home will have boundaries, which will be set either by the parent or the child. Boundaries and pampering love are not equals in relationships. Pursuing relationships can get in the way of sharing true love. Rather, a parent establishes respect for his role in the mind of a child, and the relationship will follow. A parent wrongs his child when he changes boundaries to avoid frustrations or confrontation, hoping to gain a relationship with his child.

Good relationships are difficult without boundaries, and boundaries create good relationships. The two are not opposites, but form a complementary union that produces wholeness and well-being in the child. This marriage produces the relationship a godly parent desires with his child.

Be positive and encouraging.

Every day brings us opportunities to coax our children to higher ground. If we hold positive ideals for them, they will learn to grasp them from our hands and further build their lives!

We must teach our children that the goal of life is to keep going forward, living honorably. It does not matter if we fail, if we get up, learn from the situation and move on to build. Neither does it matter if others can do the task we are attempting better than we can. We are not beaten until we refuse to get up from a fall—and go on.

We must teach our children that life is a journey. None of us perform with the perfection we crave. But the important thing is to keep going. It helps our children to live comfortably with themselves if they know that we are happy with them as imperfect people. They will never need to become like anyone else. They only need to be the best that they can be. God never requires more.

Your child will soon learn that adults also make mistakes. As he processes that, allow him to share with you any thoughts he has about the matter. Listen with your heart and mind so that the child feels heard. Then help him to deal objectively with the situation he faces in a healthy, God-honoring way. And your child will learn more about how to relate to others.

Bethany deals with a very difficult child who is not yet able to live in harmony with his world. Sometimes when she finds him doing nothing she needs to correct, she uses that opportunity to clinch another point. "Johnny," she exclaims, "I am so glad that you are not kicking anyone, or banging your head against the wall. That is wonderful!" And Johnny looks up with a wee sparkle in his eye, and smiles the tiniest bit. And sometimes he continues his harmless activity longer than usual.

Live with a humble attitude.

Parents cannot be afraid to have their children surpass them. And we cannot let our childrens' approval of us become our goal, or we will do many foolish things. A humble heart simply sees itself as it is before God, and is free from the burden of struggling with its own image. A humble parent will rejoice when his children are committed to God and are moving forward in life.

We must love our children selflessly. We sometimes tend to react to our childrens' disobedience or foolishness because we fear they have harmed our reputation. Rather, we need to make good responses out of love for the child. Sometimes the things that cause us problems stem from our own unresolved issues.

It is a wise idea to be open to suggestions from others in issues that involve our children. We are not the only ones with answers. And when we are open to ideas from others, we broaden the base of blessing for our children. We also save ourselves the heartache and damage of pretending that we are totally sufficient. When we do that, we completely miss the point with our self-centeredness. Being a parent was not designed to establish an impeccable kingdom around oneself. Rather, it places us in the position to contribute for our child's welfare.

Humility is the gift that frees us from the burdens of our carnality so that we can walk at liberty and in joy with God. It is also frees us so that we can contribute to others' lives with the same kind of wholeness.

Living in humility is the only way we can become what God intends that we will be. Only then will we be able to bless others.

Accept your child as he is right now.

The first time Hannah carried her Down's baby into church was the most difficult day she can remember. Especially when she compared Joshua to the normal infants in the nursery. One night she came to terms with God on the matter, and the days became much easier.

"I had to accept that Joshua is never going to be like most other children," Hannah explains. "To fight his handicap is only going to weigh our whole family down. I realize now that that it is not my fault that Joshua is a Down's, either. So I can go forward, meeting each day in peace because we are in God's will for our lives. And now I enjoy our special child."

We need to be okay with who our children are. We will guide and help them to become as self-sufficient and developed as they are able to be. Yet beneath that role, we must be happy and contented with who they are, instead of trying to make them into the person we wish they could be. There was no way that Hannah could make Joshua into one of the other babies who shared the nursery with him at church.

If your child is slower by nature, figure that it will take him twice as long to set the table. What does it matter if his older sibling has hands that fly rapidly at the tasks they perform? NEVER COMPARE YOUR CHILDREN. God has a purpose for each of us. When we bless each of our children as they do their best, we build sons and daughters with a wholesome sense of self-confidence.

Janet was always afraid to show her school papers to her mother. She watched with envy while her mother smiled and exclaimed over her brother's excellent work. And her heart sank to the bottom of her shoes when her mother frowned as she looked at Janet's own paper, festooned with red check marks. "Can't you do better than that?" she would ask, frowning. Yet, how could Janet—when no one understood that she had dyslexia and needed special help so she could learn to read?

We create huge problems and lots of lies in our children's minds when we expect more than they are able to produce. The dark side of this problem is that the child will feel that he can never satisfy God, and will live his life on an endless treadmill—trying to gain approval from God and others (and from himself) by being perfect. But no one can do that. We can only do the best that we can do. For Janet, at that point in her school life, that was getting twenty-five percent.

Yet, bless yourself and your children by encouraging them to aim for excellence. If we aim for nothing, that is what we will get. Life is for living. The more deposits we make, the more returns we will receive. Be realistic. Enjoy the journey, and rejoice over every small milestone that is gained. Bless the child with your love and acceptance, and invite him to share a joyful walk with you—being himself and whatever he is.

Do not belittle the child as a person. Let your children know that they have a permanent, secure relationship with you. As in marriage, you and your sons and daughters will always be a part of one another's lives. No matter what they share with you, let them know that they are accepted and beloved—simply because they have been brought into your family.

It is also important to be fair and accepting with all your children. Having favorites cuts deeply into the harmony God wants to bring into our homes. Maintain the same love and the same sense of fairness with each child. Consciously or subconsciously, they will sense the health that this brings to family life.

Receive your special child as a precious gift from God. Learn the lessons God will bring to you through this situation. And cherish the treasures that your soul will gather. God's gifts are always good.

Make your choices today thinking about the future.

It takes a lot of time to work with a handicapped child. Yet without that time commitment, your child will not become self-sufficient or learn to handle his life well. And he will lack the mental development, quality of life, and sense of accomplishment that he might have had.

When Andrea was young, her mother, Ruth, thought herself too busy to teach the child to tie her own shoes. So she quickly did the job for her.

"One day, as I tied Andrea's shoes once again, a thought struck," Ruth relates. "How many years did I want to be tying shoes for her? For the next sixty? I knew that would be unfair to Andrea or anyone who became her care provider."

That became a milestone in Ruth's parenting priorities. She began investing volumes of time in teaching Andrea to make her bed, pick up after herself, and perform self-care tasks. She also taught her daughter to do simple, useful things about the house, which made Andrea a contributing, appreciated part of the family.

It is also necessary to spend the time to teach our special children to be courteous and well-mannered. Otherwise, they (and the whole family) will suffer. Invest in the future!

Look at situations from God's eyes.

We must live with an eternal perspective. God is preparing us to spend eternity in His presence, enjoying Him. There is much that God is doing in our lives today that we will not fathom until we reach heaven. Yet God is at work in accomplishing his goals for His honor and glory, and our blessing—in the things that He brings or allows to enter our lives.

When our eyes begin to see into heaven, we will live in a way that shows that our hearts are not lost among the tangible things around us.

Only as we live with an eternal perspective can we teach our children to do the same.

God has wonderful plans for our special children in heaven. Who knows? Perhaps He is preparing them for special roles of delight even as they suffer with their handicaps. For God does not waste the pain of any of His children. Neither will God fail to bless the faithful caregivers who treasured His little ones.

Our hearts find peace, joy and rest when we are in harmony with Him. The fullness of that bliss will expand around us for eternity. May that day come soon!

chapter eighteen

Developing Reasonable Expectations

As we work with our challenged children, we want to help them achieve their highest levels of accomplishment and usefulness—while we work within their limitations. We want to teach them to live happily with who they are.

To some extent, your children will live up to your reasonable expectations. They will listen to you to find clues as to what they really can do. Encourage your child, saying "You can do it! We can at least try!" Or does your child know that you have no faith in him anyway? That you place little value on his person?

A parent's words, actions and responses will make his child feel more or less accepted. The way you love and accept your child will help promote his level of personal acceptance. When your child is at peace with himself, he will present himself in a way that will make it easier for others to accept him.

Stephen listened from the living room while his mother talked with his teacher, Sister Dorcas, on the phone. "Yes," he heard his mother say. "I understand why you would like to see Stephen relate better to his classmates. I know he seems intelligent. But he just doesn't do well socially. Stephen is different. He will never be normal."

Stephen slipped quietly out another door that did not lead to the kitchen—with a sick feeling in his stomach. The words repeated themselves over and over again in his mind. "Stephen is different. He will never be normal." He crawled into a dark corner of the barn loft, clutching his cat, while hot tears rained down his cheeks.

"What's wrong, Sonny?" A kind hand touched his shoulder, and Stephen looked up into his father's kind face.

"Mother told the teacher I will always be dumb," Stephen sniffed. "Am I dumb, Dad?"

"No, Stephen." His father put down his pitchfork and sat down beside the boy. "You can think. And you can do lots of things. Just remember how fast we cleaned the pig pens together last night. We make a good team. And you can learn more. What's the trouble?"

"The boys don't like me on the playground," Stephen exclaimed. "And yesterday I threw a stone at Billy when he laughed at me. And Sister Dorcas punished both of us."

"Hmmm." His father thought quietly for a moment. "I see you have a problem. But we can work it out. You know, if you're nice to the other boys, they'll be nicer to you. And if you have problems with the boys, make sure you tell me or your teacher."

"I will!" exclaimed Stephen. "And the next time, I won't throw stones. If the other boys don't want me, I'll go play with Tony. He likes me."

"That's the spirit!" his father replied.

Sister Dorcas was not surprised when Stephen and his father walked into her classroom the following morning. Together they made a plan for Stephen to follow in the recesses for the day.

That afternoon, Stephen went home with a smile on his face. His father and Sister Dorcas believed in him!

We often complicate things by creating sharply defined lines about what a normal person can or cannot be. We decide who is "in" or "out." It is okay to have a heart problem, but not a reading problem. People who cannot read are dumb. Having a heart problem is—well, just something normal people deal with that they're not responsible for. They are still valuable. Really?

How foolish we are! God does not divide his people into statuses. We are all people who deal with strengths and challenges. Any problems we face are simply one of the issues mankind deals with. God accepts us and deals kindly with us all. There are no classes of people with God. He is not surprised by anything that manifests in our lives.

Mary is no more responsible for her reading problem than the child who has a heart murmur is for his. She has as much personal value as any other student in the classroom. If Jason is able to finish his homework rapidly, his personal worth is no more or less than Mary's. Why do we discredit the children who try the hardest?

Always be alert when more resources are needed for the child. As I work with dyslexics, I am deeply troubled at the lack of understanding in the communities where our clients live. Schools lack adequate reading curriculum that is designed to teach a dyslexic—when it is easily available. We can limit our children because we fail to use all the resources that are at our disposal.

It is important that all of our children learn to obey. It is unfortunate when a special child is allowed to dominate family life in unhealthy ways. You may recall that Helen Keller was allowed to walk around the dining room, getting food from anyone's plate, before her teacher opened her world. Most of our challenged children are able to learn to respond to simple commands such as "Come," "Go," and "Give that to me."

When a child is able to walk and understands the meaning of the word come, he is ready for a very basic type of training. Begin by standing three feet away from Johnny with a book in your hand. Hold out your hands. Say, "Come, Johnny. Come to Mama. We will look at the book together." When he comes, say, "Good boy, Johnny. You must always come when Mama calls you." Then sit down and enjoy the book together. If the child does not come immediately, pull him toward you and repeat the command "Come" until he fully understands what is wanted.

When you know that he understands what he should be doing, progress to the next step and call Johnny to you when you do not have a book. When he comes, tell him, "Good boy, Johnny. You must always come when Mama calls you." Then hold him and kiss him, and he will understand that there are rewards for good behavior—and that he is pleasing you. When he disobeys your command, punish him—and then tell him again to come. Continue with this basic pattern over a pattern of weeks or months, but move to more difficult situations. Call the child from an adjoining room, or when he is engrossed with his toys. If you do this well and consistently, it will only be a short matter of time until Johnny learns that your word is law and leads to blessing. *Johnny is coming under authority.*

When children have learned this lesson, they are better able to move away from an extremely self-centered position. They know they are expected to fit in with and consider other people. And they are secure because you, the child's authority, are exercising your role over them.

Remember to think below the surface when your child reacts to a command in uncertainty, anger or frustration. Our most brittle children often need time to prepare for the next step. However, you must still be in charge as you deal gently with the child. Children desperately want someone to be responsible for them, who makes them accountable—and will take care of them. (See Chapter 10. Priorities for the Severely Limited Child) for a broader discussion on this subject.

We need wisdom to introduce the proactive amount of practicing and therapies. We don't want to drive our children to the point of tears and frustration. However, unless we provide part of our children's motivation, they will not develop to their full potential. Consider the child's emotional ability and choose the best time of the day for the difficult things.

Find meaningful work that fits your child. Abner and Joyce find it frustrating to do a lot of mental processing. But they work well with their hands. Abner's parents have outfitted him with a small shop where he builds cedar chests. He whistles as he sands the sweet-smelling wood. Joyce has a small bake shop. Her specialty is decorated cakes, which she does beautifully. Amy does well with children and babysits for a neighbor. Abner, Joyce and Amy all feel useful—and competent in their spheres.

How much can your child do? Be reasonable and find out. Encourage him. Believe in him. And then help him accomplish all he can from there.

Love the child God has gifted to you, and enjoy the journey!

PVC Pipe Phone Directions:

The PVC pipe phone is made by fitting two 2½" elbows together to make a "U" shaped simple auditory training unit. One end of the phone should be held to the dominant ear and the other end to the mouth. Holding the phone in this manner, the child reads aloud in a soft voice. This helps the brain do processing and memorization.

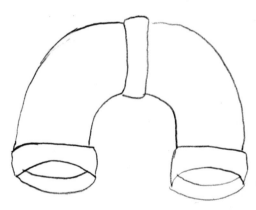